Her heart lurched in sudden panic

"My feelings for Steve have nothing to do with you," she said firmly.

"Oh, I'd say they have a great deal to do with me, Kate," Luke said. "As you're beginning to realize, I'm flesh and blood, and no memory in the world can make you feel the way you did just now."

Her cheeks blazed scarlet. "It won't happen again, Mr. Redmond, that's a promise. Just put it down to a moment of irrational weakness."

His mouth twisted derisively. "Call it what you like, Kate, but don't make promises that you can't, and I certainly don't intend, to keep."

Design for Love

Jean Evans

Harlequin Books

TORONTO • NEW YORK • LONDON
AMSTERDAM • PARIS • SYDNEY • HAMBURG
STOCKHOLM • ATHENS • TOKYO • MILAN

Original hardcover edition published in 1988
by Mills & Boon Limited

ISBN 0-373-17029-7

Harlequin Romance first edition January 1989

Copyright © 1988 by Jean Evans.
All rights reserved. Except for use in any review, the reproduction or utilization
of this work in whole or in part in any form by any electronic, mechanical or
other means, now known or hereafter invented, including xerography,
photocopying and recording, or in any information storage or retrieval system,
is forbidden without the permission of the publisher, Harlequin Enterprises
Limited, 225 Duncan Mill Road, Don Mills, Ontario, Canada M3B 3K9.

All the characters in this book have no existence outside the imagination of
the author and have no relation whatsoever to anyone bearing the same name
or names. They are not even distantly inspired by any individual known or
unknown to the author, and all incidents are pure invention.

® are Trademarks registered in the United States Patent and Trademark Office
and in other countries.

Printed in U.S.A.

CHAPTER ONE

'KATE, this is Mike.' The voice came urgently over the answering machine. 'Where the hell are you? I've been trying to reach you all morning. Look, something's going on I think you should know about. Try to make the meeting, there's a good girl.'

Kate Langley's fingers drummed impatiently against the steering wheel, as yet another set of traffic lights changed to red.

'Oh, come on.' London's rush hour and a June heatwave were doing nothing to sweeten tempers, her own included. The smell of dust and traffic fumes was intense. She took her hands from the wheel to lift the heavy swathe of ash-blonde hair from her neck, but the relief it brought was almost non-existent.

The lights changed to green. Two cars edged forwards. The lights were red again. Behind her, a taxi had his radio playing at full blast. Kate reached across to the passenger seat for her briefcase. She felt hot and cross, and Mike's cryptic message had come at the end of a long, frustrating morning. It wasn't as if she knew *why* she was making this headlong dash across the city.

She thumbed through the pages of her diary, one eye warily on the traffic lights. There was nothing about a meeting scheduled between herself and

Halliday's until next week, when she was supposed to discuss the plans for the layouts she had drawn up for the new reception area. She nibbled at her lower lip and, without even being aware of what she was doing, turned to glare at the driver of the Porsche which slid soundlessly alongside her own car. It really was too bad of Mike. Unlike him, too. She wondered briefly what could have prompted the message, as she let her gaze drift idly to the man in the Porsche.

It seemed unfair that anyone could look so cool and unruffled in such heat, especially in the dark, expensively cut suit he was wearing. He stared straight ahead, giving a clear view of his profile, and Kate found herself staring at strong, chiselled features, a straight, classical nose and jet-black hair which, with the sun-bronzed complexion made her wonder whether there might be some foreign blood—Italian or Greek, perhaps—in him.

He turned to look directly at her, and for several seconds Kate looked into thickly lashed, piercingly dark eyes which, at this moment, were filled with sardonic amusement. With a quick intake of breath she looked away, conscious, as her cheeks tinged with pink, that she had been staring, and worse, that for several seconds he had blatantly returned that look.

She fumbled clumsily with the gears, realising that the lights had changed to green, and suffered the ignominy of seeing the Porsche glide ahead, the driver's hand raised in a brief but mocking salute as he pulled away, leaving her struggling ahead of a line of impatient taxi drivers, all blaring their car horns.

'Capitalist pig.' Kate's mouth compressed as she

found the right gear and sent the Mini juddering forwards into the mainstream of traffic. One of the drivers stuck his head out of his cab window, making a suggestion which added to the heat in her cheeks. 'And you, too,' she muttered.

Grinding her teeth, she stared purposefully ahead, and didn't relax until she saw her turning, then manoeuvred her way out and drew up alongside the block which housed the Halliday's Hotel empire.

Grabbing her bag and briefcase, she headed for the doors, narrowly missing a crowd of office staff heading for a late lunch. She tried to ignore the rumblings of hunger in her own stomach. Missed lunches were something she had learned to live with in the past five years.

She walked straight through the swing doors, pausing briefly at the desk, where a harassed receptionist finished putting through a call before looking up and recognising her. 'Oh, Miss Langley, I didn't know you were expected today. I'm afraid Mr Halliday isn't in.'

'That's all right, Jane, This isn't a scheduled meeting. I got a call from Mike Forrest asking me to come over.'

'Oh, yes, of course. So you know, then?' Jane Robart pressed a neatly manicured finger on the intercom button and shook her head sadly. 'I'm afraid it's all come as a bit of a shock. Ah, Mr Forrest, Miss Langley is here in reception.' She turned to Kate. 'You can go straight up. You know where.'

Feeling slightly bemused, Kate thanked her. 'I take it he's in the boardroom?'

'No.' Jane swung to answer the phone, cupping a hand over the receiver. 'The meeting finished nearly an hour ago. He's in his office.'

'Damn!' Kate frowned her displeasure. 'OK, thanks, Jane.' She turned and headed for the door, a tall, slender figure with swinging ash-blonde hair and grey-green eyes, a small, uptilted nose and a generous mouth which, at this moment, bore a hint of determination.

Mike Forrest's office was at the end of the corridor, but she heard the raised voices long before she reached it. The door was ajar and she paused for a second, suddenly reluctant to intrude as she heard Mike's own voice, clipped and sharp with tension.

'So what the hell do you suggest I do? You don't imagine I'm exactly over the moon about what's happened, surely?'

'Well, you must have had some inkling. A thing like this can't happen overnight, without warning.' That was Lorna Carrington, the Hotel Empire's Personnel Manager, sounding dangerously close to tears.

Kate tapped firmly at the door and went in. 'Sorry to intrude, but the door was open.'

'Kate.' Mike stood up, his face a study of relief as he went to met her, and it was easy to see why. Lorna Carrington's eyes held a distinct trace of tears.

She blew her nose hard. 'I'm sorry. We were so busy arguing, I'm afraid we didn't notice.'

'I—er—did knock.'

'It's OK, Kate.' Mike ran a hand wearily through his hair. 'You're not interrupting anything, certainly nothing that isn't common knowledge by now, anyway.'

'My God, that's a joke!' Lorna's laugh was bitter. 'I'm beginning to think I was the last person in the world to see it coming, and someone hasn't been exactly honest.'

'Would someone mind telling me what's going on?' Kate looked from one to the other as she dropped her briefcase on to the nearest chair. 'I got your message when I went back to the office, Mike, and if I may say so, its content left a lot to be desired. Couldn't you have been a little more explicit, instead of expecting me to drop everything and hare across London in this traffic?'

'Sorry about that. Things moved a bit faster than I'd anticipated.'

'I'd say that was probably the understatement of the year.' Lorna threw him a scathing look. 'If you said we'd been hit by an avalanche, you might be a shade closer to the truth!'

'For heaven's sake, do you have to keep rubbing it in? How the hell do you think *I* feel?'

'Look,' Kate intervened hastily, 'I hate to break this up, but you still haven't explained what's going on. I take it I have been called here for some particular reason, not just to act as referee while you two sling insults at each other?'

They both subsided, looking shamefaced, but it was Mike who looked at Kate and explained. 'Unfortunately she's right,' he said, tersely. 'I don't know quite how to say this.'

'Why not try straight out?' Kate suggested. 'It might save time.'

Mike looked at her for a second, then shrugged. 'We've been taken over—lock, stock and barrel.' He got up from the desk where he had been half sitting. 'I'm sorry, there's no nicer way to put it.'

'How about "sold down the drain"?' Lorna flashed him an angry look and reached for her hanky again. Kate stared at Mike for several seconds as, for a while, his words failed to register; then, slowly, as if he had physically hit her, she reached for a chair and sat down. 'You're not serious?'

'Oh, he's serious all right.' Lorna reached across the desk for a cigarette, her eyes snapping with impatience. She was an attractive woman, tall, slim, probably in her early forties—Kate had never been sure. 'We were given the glad tidings this morning. *Told*, mind you, not consulted. By the time we got to hear about it, the whole deal had been signed and sealed, and *we* were delivered. It was a complete shock. Well, to most of us, anyway.' She flung a look at Mike and turned away, her hands shaking as she fumbled with a lighter.

Kate looked at Mike, almost afraid to speak. 'Is it true?'

He dug his hands in his pockets. 'That's why I left the message. Management called an extraordinary general meeting to break the news. I reckoned that, as you had as much at stake in this as anyone, you had a right to know what was going on.'

Kate swallowed hard. 'I'm still not sure I do understand, Mike.' Her eyes mirrored her confusion. 'How could it happen?'

'Join the club.' Lorna blew a cloud of smoke into

the air. 'We seem to be an élite few.'

'But Halliday's is a huge enterprise.'

'Huge, maybe—but they haven't been doing so well lately.'

Mikes face was grim. 'If we're honest, I suppose we've all seen it happening, but we chose not to put any interpretation on falling bookings and poor customer relations.'

'Oh, come on, you can be more honest than that,' Lorna said, cuttingly. 'This firm hasn't progressed in the past thirty years.'

'But surely that's not exactly true?' Kate challenged. 'I mean, there *has* been some sign that they were at least trying. What about the designs I've been working on for the new reception area, and the talks about changing the company's image nationally?'

'Kate, it's no good.' Mike seemed to be having difficulty meeting her gaze. She wondered why as she flung him a look of silent appeal which, for some reason, went unanswered.

She looked at the older woman. Lorna Carrington shrugged and turned away. 'Mike?' Colour darkened Kate's face. 'I have a contract . . .?'

'For what it's worth,' he said tautly. 'Hell, I'm sorry. Legally, of course, it will have to be honoured—you won't lose financially, but that's the only hope I can give.'

'Financially!' Kate's mouth suddenly felt very dry. 'But what about all the work on the designs? They can't do this!'

'They've done it. It wasn't on the agenda, but I brought the matter up myself at the meeting this

this morning. I forced the issue . . .' His mouth tightened. 'I'm sorry, but I'm afraid it looks as if the new management call the tune. They have to pay you for the contracted work, but they have their own development programme and schedule already worked out.' He dragged a hand through his hair. 'I don't know where, if at all, you'll come into it. My hands are tied.'

Kate's voice held a note of quiet desperation. 'Three months of damned hard work have gone into those designs. They had the board's full approval. I was told to go ahead and do the costings, I was even sticking to the financial guidelines set out by Halliday's themselves.'

'Yes, well, now we know why they were so low.' Lorna looked pityingly at Kate's ashen face. 'It was all a whitewash, a con, to stop us and everyone else from guessing the truth—that Halliday's were broke.'

Kate passed a hand shakily over her forehead. 'I can't believe this is happening, how *could* it happen . . . you mean it was all lies?'

'That's right. You've been had, as they say, along with the rest of us, or most of us, at any rate.'

'For heaven's sake, do you have to put it so crudely?' Mike said drily.

Lorna's eyes narrowed. 'Frankly, I can't think of any other way.'

Kate felt sick. Reaching for her briefcase, she took out a large file and tossed it on to the desk. 'Well, I guess these aren't going to be much use.' She sighed, biting at her lower lip. 'I've worked myself almost to a standstill trying to get them right. My God, how am

I going to explain it to Sue? We've sweated blood to get this design agency to where it is now. I don't know what this is going to do to us.'

Mike shifted uncomfortably. 'Believe me, a lot of other people around here feel the same way right now.' He looked tired and suddenly older. 'I don't know much about this Redmond guy yet, but what little I do know makes me realise he's the sort who deals strictly with percentages, not people.'

'Redmond?' Kate echoed hollowly.

'Luke Redmond,' Lorna supplied caustically. 'Head hatchet man for Poseidon International, our new bosses. And when I say hatchet man, I mean hatchet. Believe me, he doesn't waste any time. The redundancy notices are already being prepared.'

'You're not serious?'

'You don't think so?' Lorna ground the remnants of her cigarette into the ashtray. 'Then I suggest you talk to the fifty who'll be getting theirs today.'

Kate turned to look at Mike, knowing the colour had drained from her face. 'Surely he can't do that?'

'Oh, take it from me,' Lorna answered for him, 'our Mr Redmond is an expert. He didn't even show for this morning's meeting, but then he has people who do his dirty work for him.'

'But what about the people who've been here for most of their working lives?'

Lorna laughed scathingly. 'You don't imagine a man like that has any conscience?'

'Oh, come on, Lorna!' Mike intervened sharply. 'This is business, not personal, and we're not getting anywhere like this.'

'Maybe not,' she rounded on him, 'but then, *you're* not out of a job.'

Kate's gaze flew from one to the other in questioning disbelief. 'You don't mean . . . You're not . . .'

Lorna's mouth twisted. 'As good as. Oh, I've been offered a cosy little number up in Birmingham.'

Mike's mouth tightened. 'Don't just dismiss it out of hand. Poseidon have hotels and conference facilities worldwide.'

'Yes, but we're not talking worldwide. We're talking Birmingham, and you're not the one who's going to have to start again.' Lorna smiled bleakly at Kate. 'Sorry about this. You could say it's been one of those days, and thanks to Mr Redmond I doubt if my life will ever be quite the same again.' She reached for her bag and headed for the door. 'I'm going to get some coffee. I may even take an extended lunch hour, and if anyone wants me, frankly I don't give a damn.' She paused at the door. 'Perhaps we can meet for a consolatory drink.'

Kate nodded. 'I'd like that.'

Mike pushed the door to a close and went to sit heavily in the chair behind the desk. 'Sorry about that. She's obviously a bit uptight.'

Kate gave a half laugh of incredulity. 'Honestly, Mike, I don't blame her. I'm feeling more than a little uptight myself right now.' She paced to the window and back, her movements unconsciously graceful, in spite of her agitation. 'I don't understand how it could happen. What sort of a man can do a thing like this?'

Mike seemed to find her anger embarrassing. 'I think they simply didn't believe it would happen.

Maybe I should have tried to warn you, but I didn't believe it, either. I don't think any of us realised how ruthless this Redmond was.' He put his arms round her. 'I feel so damned guilty.'

Kate frowned at a thought too fleeting even to grasp, then shook her head as she turned in the circle of his arms. 'I just feel so frustrated, so *angry*. Sue and I have worked so hard, and now this! It's not the money, it's the wasted time and effort.' She closed her eyes, resting her head briefly against his shoulder. 'It's all so bloody unfair.' She had to swallow hard to hold back the threatening tears, as Mike traced the line of her cheek and throat, and her response was purely instinctive as his mouth came down over hers.

Her relationship with Mike had developed slowly over the past three mouths, on her part at least. She had guessed almost from the beginning that his own interest in her was more physical, of course, but she had been too unsure of her own feelings—still was, for that matter—to let it develop beyond the occasional date and a few kisses.

She was aware—how could she not be?—that for Mike it was becoming increasingly unsatisfactory, but he hadn't so far made any attempt to rush her, sensing that Steve's death was still too fresh in her mind.

'It may not be as bad as it seems now,' Mike breathed into her hair.

Kate wasn't fooled by the attempt at reassurance. 'Let's face it, as far as Poseidon are concerned, I'm one small fish in a tiny pool.' Her mouth twisted. 'One thing's for sure, though, I'd give anything to meet this great god himself, face to face, just to see what sort of bastard it is who plays with other people's lives like this.' Her cheeks flushed. 'I'd like to tell Mr Luke Redmond precisely what I think of him.

'I'm sure I'd find the experience most enlightening.'

At the sound of the voice coming from behind her, Kate spun round, her attention riveted on the man standing in the doorway, and felt as if an electric current had passed through her body. It wasn't just the overwhelming sense of power and self-assurance which seemed to emanate from him as he stood there, though that in itself was sufficient to send a shiver of awareness running down her spine, nor was it the blatant arrogance with which he regarded her as, for several seconds, their gazes met and held. It was something in the piercingly dark eyes which raked her slender figure and delicate features with an intensity so vibrantly sexual that it almost took her breath away.

He came slowly into the room, tall, slim and muscular, so that she was immediately conscious of every line, from the taut shoulders to a slender waist and lean thighs beneath the dark trousers he was wearing. She was also aware, as the flush darkened her cheeks, that she had seen this man before. He had been driving the Porsche and, even as the steel-dark eyes bored deeply into hers, she also knew, with a terrible sinking feeling, that this must be Luke Redmond!

With a determined effort, she dragged her gaze up to meet his. 'You!' She moistened her suddenly dry lips and his eyes narrowed, as if to mock what he knew to be an air of assumed self-confidence.

'Dare I say, we must stop meeting like this?' he drawled, the expression in his dark eyes hidden by thickly lashed, hooded lids.

Kate's throat felt painfully tight. Seen close to, the black hair was even darker than she had imagined, longer, too, as it curled slightly over the collar of his blue shirt. There was something infinitely forbidding about the sculptured mouth and aquiline nose.

She cleared her throat with difficulty. 'It woud be a little corny, don't you think?'

Mike hovered uncomfortably. 'Am I to take it you two know each other?'

Luke Redmond gave a husky laugh, showing teeth which looked startlingly white against the deeply tanned features.

'That may be putting it a little strongly.' The narrow gaze was directed straight at Kate, and she felt her blush deepen. 'You could say we were more like ships that pass in the night, except that, unlike most shipboard encounters, ours is becoming increasingly intriguing.'

Kate almost choked with embarrassment as, for some reason, he seemed deliberately to be giving Mike a false impression. Her chin rose.

'I take it you *are* Luke Redmond? In which case, I suppose I owe you an apology. You weren't suppose to overhear.'

'No?' The dark eyebrows rose, and she found herself subjected to a yet greater, flagrantly masculine appraisal as his gaze swept over her with calculating ruthlessness. 'But then, they do say listeners never hear anything good of themselves.'

'Obviously *they* are right,' she shot at him sweetly, and intercepted a quelling look from Mike.

'Mr Redmond, this is Kate Langley, and despite what you may think, it wasn't quite the way it seems. It was a mistake . . . a misunderstanding.'

Kate's eyes flashed dark green. 'Don't get involved in this, Mike, please. I'm quite capable of fighting my own battles.'

'Isn't there something in the rules about firing a warning salvo first?' Luke Redmond's voice was a soft drawl, and Kate wished she coud back away from the tantalising smell of expensive aftershave as he moved imperceptibly closer.

'I wouldn't know.' She flung the challenge, but stood transfixed. 'I don't believe in taking prisoners. I always aim to kill.'

This time the dark eyes narrowed cynically. 'I shall have to remember that, but I also give you fair warning, Miss Langley, I play by very different rules, and I'm certainly not averse to taking prisoners when I know that, sooner or later, it will get me what I want.'

Kate shivered, aware that there was something about this man that seemed to offer a threat, even though, as yet, she couldn't decide precisely what that threat was. Everything about him, from the tall, tautly muscled physique to the arrogant good looks spelled sex appeal. There was no denying that Luke Redmond had the kind of looks that would appeal to any woman—except herself, she thought decisively. Right now, she wasn't interested. She certainly didn't like being threatened.

'Oh, I don't doubt it, Mr Redmond.' Kate's chin rose. 'I'm already beginning to discover the sort of methods you use, and frankly I don't care for them. My God, there must be a word for your kind of double dealing . . . your cold-blooded wrecking of people's lives.'

'For God's sake, Kate!' Mike's face was white. 'You don't know what you're saying . . .'

She shook him off, aware of Luke Redmond watching her, his face without expression. 'I know exactly what I'm saying, and so, I think, does Mr Redmond.' She waited warily. He looked far too calm. 'At least you'll note he hasn't bothered to deny any of it so far. Now, why is that, do you suppose? Could it be because he knows it's true?'

The arrogant mockery had gone from Luke Redmond's face now, leaving pure anger as he towered over her. His gaze swept to Mike. He walked to the door, opening it. *'Out.'*

With one tense look in her direction, Mike went, leaving her to face Luke Redmond alone. Her lips trembled briefly as she saw the aggressive thrust of his jaw.

'I'd strongly advise you to watch what you say.' The words were softly spoken, yet Kate was left in no doubt whatsoever that they held a threat. For a second she hesitated, but no longer. She wasn't going to allow herself to be intimidated, especially by a total stranger.

'Why?' She met the dark, brooding gaze, and wished she hadn't as she became instantly aware of the determination written there. She swallowed hard.

'You've already as good as put me out of a job, along with plenty of others. But then, you don't care about that, do you, Mr Redmond?' She tossed her head, looking up at him. 'So what more can you possibly do?'

He didn't move. Instead, he gave her a long, searching look which sent the colour rushing into her face. Exasperated, she tried to move away, only to find her path blocked as he placed himself deliberately between herself and the door. Then, without a word of warning, his hand came up to grasp her chin, forcing her to look at him. 'Oh, I'm sure I could come up with a number of intriguing possibilities.'

Kate gasped slightly as the mere contact of his hand seemed to burn against her skin. She pushed him away. 'Oh, I'm sure you could, Mr Redmond. I don't doubt you're a man of considerable talents in certain directions, but you may as well get one thing straight from the start. These tactics may work with your other women, but I'm not interested. I'm immune to your kind of charm, Mr Redmond. Frankly, it leaves me cold.'

His eyebrows rose in a half-pained, half-mocking grimace. 'I'd like to know on what basis you presume to judge my . . . er . . . talents, Miss Langley. You really ought to sample the goods before claiming indifference. You might even surprise yourself and find the experience far more rewarding than you think. Or perhaps you've just been soured by some past experience? In which case, you shouldn't make the mistake of thinking that all men make lousy lovers.'

Kate gasped as if he had physically struck her. For a split second, she closed her eyes, fighting a sense of panic as from somewhere, deep down, a familiar, dull ache began to claw its way upwards. An ache which had lain dormant for so long that, naïvely, she had imagined it was gone for ever. Until now. Her face was deathly white as she opened her eyes and, before she was even aware of what she was doing, her hand flew up to strike him across the face in a blind fury which left a savage imprint across his cheek.

But his own reaction was equally swift. Without as much as a change of expression, his fingers closed over her wrist in a vice-like grip which made her cry out with pain.

'Why, you . . . bastard!' She spat the words through clenched teeth as she struggled to free herself. But, the more she fought, the tighter his grip became. He towered over her, dark, menacing, utterly ruthless, as he forced her closer and still closer. She was aware of the taut, sensuous mouth hovering just above her own, and he laughed in a way that sent shivers running down her spine.

'I'm sorry you did that, Kate, because I warned you what would happen.'

She struggled, frightened as much by the wild racing of her own heart as by the brutal strength with which he held her. He jerked her closer still, until she couldn't help but be aware of the dangerous strength of his thighs as he moulded her to him, his hands at the base of her spine, arching her relentlessly against him.

She tried to pull away, shocked by his sensuality,

and her own traitorous response to it. 'I don't know what you're talking about.'

His dark eyes glittered dangerously. 'I warned you that I play by my own rules, and I just took my first prisoner.'

She fought him out of sheer desperation. 'You're crazy! Let me go.' She had known this man for less than an hour, yet he was arousing a multitude of emotions in her which, until now, she had imagined were safely hidden, and she had every intention of keeping it that way. Her eyes flashed like green fire but, to her chagrin. Luke Redmond's dark eyes merely filled with amusement.

'Oh, I'll let you go, Kate. But first we're going to talk. *Now.*' He nodded towards the door. 'We'll go somewhere nice and quiet, where there's no danger of our being disturbed. You've flung a lot of accusations at me, Kate Langley, aside from casting aspersions on my masculinity.'

'I did no such thing,' Kate rasped. 'I assure you, your sexual prowess—or lack of it—doesn't interest me in the least.'

His eyes narrowed as he chuckled softly. 'Careful, Kate, your claws are showing. Remember your namesake.'

She blinked. 'My namesake?'

'Another Kate?'

She gasped as his hand tightened about her wrist. 'I don't know what you're talking about, and you're hurting me.'

His grip relaxed slightly. 'She was a shrew too, Kate, until some man came along and tamed her.'

'Why you . . . how dare you!'

Releasing her, the sardonic gaze swept over her flushed features. 'You'd be surprised what I dare do, Miss Langley, especially when provoked. And for some reason, since the minute I set eyes on you, I've found you definitely and utterly provocative.'

Kate licked her dry lips nervously, telling herself this was all part of some crazy nightmare, and that at any minute she would wake up to find herself at home, safely tucked up in her own bed. Except that, for some reason, the association linking bed and Luke Redmond was equally disturbing! 'I don't even know you!' she snapped.

'That's right, you don't.' He walked towards her, closing the gap she would have preferred to keep between them. 'Any more than I know you. But before you leave this office that's something I definitely intend to rectify. I'm not used to being called a liar and a cheat, especially by a complete stranger, even a very beautiful stranger. I think that deserves some answers—some form of retribution too, don't you?'

Kate paled at his blatant assessment of her slender figure, pale blonde hair and wide, green eyes. Her lips parted in angry protest, only to die as she sensed that in any battle with this man she could never win. Everything about him suggested arrogance, even the way he stood, legs apart, supremely confident of his own physical superiority.

She frowned. 'I'm not afraid of you or your bullying tactics.'

'Really?' he said softly. 'Then perhaps you should

be. As for my bullying tactics,' he shook his head, 'there you go again, Kate, misjudging me. When you get to know me better, you'll realise that I never have to resort to bullying in order to get what I want.' His hands were on her arms, then her neck, then his fingers laced through her hair as he held her face, forcing her to look at him. 'I can think of far subtler methods.'

His mouth hovered, swooped lower. She caught the smell of his aftershave again, was aware of the warmth of his body as he drew her closer. The dark eyes lazily searched her delicate, oval face, frowning briefly at the suggestion of panic in her eyes, and putting his own interpretation on it before the sensual mouth closed over hers in a kiss which she did her best to avoid, twisting her head away, her hands pressed against his chest.

'I won't hurt you.' He muttered the words against her hair before ruthlessly gripping her chin and forcing her mouth to meet his. She had expected a brutal kiss; instead it was gentle, teasing, as he made a slow exploration of her lips and throat. She moaned softly in protest as his hand went to her hair, twining into the thickness of it, caressing her shoulders.

For several seconds, Kate froze with shock and, almost as if he sensed her resistance, the kiss became deliberately more insistent, more demanding. She drew a shuddering breath as it became a savage assault on her emotions, the punishment he had promised. Luke Redmond was an expert, a deadly, dangerous expert and, physically, she knew, she hadn't the strength to fight him. Mentally, she had had five years in which to build barriers and she had no intention of allowing any man to drag them down again.

With a supreme effort, she broke away, dragging her mouth from the plundering assault to stand shivering, her eyes dark green smudges of fear in the whiteness of her face. He released her, abruptly. The lines of his face were deep and rugged as he stared at her with a look so penetrating that she had the feeling he could see right into her soul. Unbidden, colour flooded into her face.

'Satisfied, Mr Redmond?' She drew a shaky breath, fighting to stem the threatening tears.

'Oh, I wouldn't say that, Miss Langley.' Her show of temper only seemed to amuse him. 'Let's just say it was an . . . interesting experience.'

'Well, I hope you made the most of it, because it's the last you're likely to get at my expense. I warned you, I'm immune.'

Dark brows rose. 'You may fool yourself, Kate, but you can't fool me. I don't know what—or who—is responsible for that ice-cold front you put up, but I do know it doesn't go as deep as you might care to think.'

She gasped. 'Why are you doing this? Why me?'

'Let's just say, I can't resist a challenge.'

'I see.' Her fists clenched. 'You mean, if I fell into your arms, or your bed, you'd soon lose interest?'

'That isn't what I said, though it's certainly an interesting proposition!' His eyes glinted with quiet laughter and Kate drew an angry breath.

'You flatter yourself, Mr Redmond. That wasn't a proposition. I was merely letting you know that I recognise your type, and, much as I hate to disappoint you, I don't play that sort of game.' She faced him, surprised to find herself still shaking. 'To be perfectly honest, I find your attitude rather boring and, if I may say so, a little outdated.'

He moved with a speed that made her gasp then, gripping her arms so that she winced with pain. 'My God, Kate, whoever he is, he's done a really good job on you, hasn't he? You're so screwed up inside, I doubt if you're capable of any genuine emotion.' His eyes searched her pale face. 'Or is it just that you're too damned scared that if you let go you might actually feeling something?'

She felt the colour drain from her face, and swayed slightly as she dragged her wrist free of the imprisoning fingers. Ice-cold eyes met dark green ones as the tears welled up. Her head went up in one last desperate challenge before she turned, needing to get away before he could see the tears spilling on to her cheeks.

'I'm happy to say that's something you'll never find out, *Mister* Redmond,' she said, her throat taut with misery. 'And for your information, it's *Mrs* Langley, not Miss. But then, I don't suppose that matters either, to a man like you.

CHAPTER TWO

FOR several seconds, Luke Redmond didn't move. Then, in two swift strides, he had reached the door ahead of Kate, slamming it to a close before he swung her to face him. Firm hands grasped her arms, pinning them to her sides when she would have struggled. His mouth was taut with anger. 'What did you say?' he bit out.

Kate felt her heart hammering in her chest as she fought the sense of panic rising within her. Strands of hair clung to her damp cheek, but she couldn't brush them away. The mocking laughter had gone from his face now, leaving his expression taut, his mouth a grim line.

She tried to lever him away, but the movement only brought his hard-muscled body into closer contact, as he held her pinned against the door. 'Please . . . let me go.'

'Not until you say it again.'

She gritted her teeth, wishing she could move her face from the close proximity of his mouth and the threat it seemed to offer. 'I think you heard me, Mr Redmond. Why so shocked? Or is your ego so over-inflated that you can't believe a woman might genuinely find your advances objectionable?'

His eyes glittered as he looked down at her.

'Modesty may not be my strongest suit, but I do know when a woman responds, Kate. And you did.'

With groan, she tore herself from his grasp to stand, shaking, as far from him as possible. 'That's not true.' She stared at him. It *couldn't* be true. There was only room for one man in her life, and that man was, and would always be, Steve.

She swallowed hard, and only realised she was actually crying when she tasted the salt on her lips. 'Damn you!'

His gaze narrowed sharply. 'For God's sake, Kate, it was a kiss. We didn't go to bed together, much as the idea appeals.'

Her eyes widened, then she turned away, as much from the mockery in his tone as from a brief but breathtaking vision of herself in this man's bed. 'You don't understand.'

'Don't I?' He was beside her again, forcing her to look at him. 'Perhaps you're right, but if it's an apology you're waiting for you'll have a long wait, *Mrs* Langley. If there's one thing I never apologise for it's kissing a beautiful woman, especially one who was just asking for it.'

'That's a lie,' she said raggedly.

'Is it?' he asked, his mouth twisting bitterly. 'If you have the same effect on your husband as you have on me, I can understand how he'd be scared to death every time he lets you out of his sight. He must be quite something. Does it please you to know I'm jealous, Kate?'

She stood with her back pressed against the door, feeling the tears force their way out from beneath her tightly closed lashes as she felt herself falling into the grey, suffocating mists of an old, familiar nightmare. In her mind's eye, it happened all over again. Steve . . . the car . . . the policeman arriving to tell her about the accident and, after that, the pain and guilt which had taken years to turn into the kind of numbness of both body and mind which had made living more bearable. Until now, when this man had unknowingly but none the less savagely re-opened the wound.

She stared at him, her expression haunted, filled with pain. 'My husband was killed in a car accident, five years ago. Does that satisfy your curiosity, or are there any more questions?'

Just for an instant, a look of compassion filled his eyes, then he shook his head. 'No, no questions. But don't you think five years is a long time to grieve for anyone with such intensity?'

She pulled away from him, her eyes flashing. 'And what would you know about grief, Mr Redmond? You accuse me of being screwed up, but I doubt if you're capable of a single unselfish emotion. The only thing you understand is brute force, so what's your particular hang-up?' she taunted.

His eyes narrowed. 'I believe in getting what I want.'

'Oh, yes, I can believe that.' Kate shivered. There was something about Luke Redmond which made her feel vulnerable. 'If I needed proof, which I don't, I'd only have to look at the way you walked in here. You took over this company without a word of warning, and without as much as a thought for what it might do to people's lives.'

His mouth tightened. 'Even if that were true, which it isn't, no matter what you think of me, you're not that naïve. You must know it couldn't have happened without a lot of prior negotiation.'

She frowned, confused by the quiet note of certainty in hes voice. 'Then why was it kept so quiet?'

'It wasn't.'

'Oh, come on!' she scorned. 'Am I really supposed to believe that?'

He shrugged, turning to sit on the edge of the desk. 'I'm telling you the facts, which I assume you could just as easily get from Forrest. Poseidon International were in the market for a takeover of Halliday's weeks ago. Admittedly, it hasn't been shouted from the rooftops. We weren't looking for competition, and Halliday's . . .' He shrugged. 'Let's just say they weren't looking to broadcast falling bookings.'

'And you were more than eager to take advantage of the situation, I'm sure,' said Kate mockingly.

His mouth twisted derisively. 'Business is business, Kate. I don't know on what your relationship with Forrest is built, but it must have struck you that he could have kept you in the picture more.'

'There is no *relationship*, Mr Redmond.'

He laughed softly. 'But not for lack of enthusiasm on his part, I dare say?' The dark eyes studied her flushed cheeks, and she drew in a long, steadying breath.

'Let's leave Mike out of this, shall we?'

'Oh, I'd be delighted. I much prefer a clear field, though I'm not averse to removing the opposition myself if I see the need.'

Startled, Kate looked directly into the taunting features, and felt a tremor of something closely akin to excitement run through her. No matter how much she might dislike Luke Redmond and all he stood for, there was no denying that he possessed a kind of animal magnetism which, at any other time, she might have found hard to resist. As it was, she gasped at the sheer arrogance behind his words. Her eyes clouded with wariness and she took a step back. Almost as if he had read her thoughts, Luke laughed.

'Don't worry, Kate, I don't intend making love to you here and now. I don't believe in rushing things. Some things are better taken slowly.'

'Mr Redmond,' Kate managed in a suffocated voice, all too aware of the hot colour suffusing her cheeks, 'if you were the last man on earth . . .'

'If I were the last man on earth, Kate, I'd make you beg me to make love to you. Some day, I swear, you will.'

'Never!' she spat the word at him and watched the full, sensuous mouth twist with amusement.

'Never is a very long time, Kate. Be patient.'

'Oh, I assure you, patience is one of my very strong suits, Mr Redmond. I'll wait for ever.' Her mouth set rebelliously, and for a second his eyes darkened. She wished he would move away from the door so that she could escape. When he didn't, it was she who put some distance between them. From the window, she turned to look at him. 'I don't suppose you've given a thought to those people who've worked here most of their lives, have you? Or don't they count to someone as ruthless as you?'

His eyebrow rose. 'You've changed the subject, Kate. What's the matter? Scared?'

'Just answer the question, Mr Redmond, if you can.'

'Oh, I *can*. It's more a case of whether I choose to, but since you ask so nicely . . .' He looked at her coolly. 'There was bound to be dead wood.'

'Dead wood?' Her eyes widened with disbelief. 'Oh, yes, and you lost no time in pruning it, did you? Well, I hope your conscience keeps you awake at night.'

Luke's eyes filled with amusement as he looked at her. 'I hate to disappoint you, but I never have any trouble sleeping.'

'That's probably because you don't *possess* a conscience,' she flung at him. 'People aren't people to you, they're just . . . possessions, things.'

The expression in his eyes was unreadable as he looked at her. 'You might be surprised to find there are some things even I care very deeply about. But then, you don't know anything about me—yet. I suppose *I'll* just have to learn to be patient, too, until you learn to trust me.'

Kate felt her cheeks redden at an implication she didn't even dare begin to acknowledge. 'Just don't hold your breath, Mr Redmond. It could be a long wait.'

'My friends call me Luke.'

'How nice for them. I'm surprised you have any.'

He gave a soft, throaty chuckle. 'You certainly don't give in gracefully, do you?'

Kate stiffened. The hard cynicism had gone from his expression, but somehow the quiet laughter she saw now was all the more disturbing. Confusion briefly furrowed her brow. Luke Redmond hid his thoughts too well beneath that cool, arrogant gaze. He was an enigma, and she didn't like enigmas. What kind of man was he really? she wondered. Something about the sensuous mouth and the firm line of his jaw sent a violent and totally unexpected fire rushing through her as she stared at him, and she clamped her lips into a rigid, nervous line.

She came back to reality as she realised he was returning her stare with equal intensity, though any conclusions he might have drawn from the careful scrutiny were hidden.

'I've learned the hard way to stand on my own feet,' she retorted swiftly. 'It may surprise you to hear it, but equality for women in business is still a fallacy. Oh, the opportunities are there, but I soon discovered it doesn't pay to be soft. There are always people ready to take advantage.'

'It's a hard world out there,' he rasped. 'If you can't stand the heat, get out of the kitchen.'

'I'm not looking for sympathy.'

'And I'm not offering any.' His mouth twisted. 'But I *am* curious.'

'About what?' she asked, warily.

'About why interior design?'

'Because it's what I'm good at,' she said defensively. She half expected him to make some challenge, but he remained silent. 'I went to art college—originally, the idea was to paint.' Her mouth curved into an involuntary smile. 'Fortunately, I discovered fairly early on that, while I had some talent, I was never going to be anything exceptional.' She made a careless gesture with her hand. 'Oh, I played around at it for a while, telling myself I could improve my technique, that it would come right with a little perseverence. But after a while I stopped fooling myself.' She turned to look at him, brushing the hair back from her face, and suddenly the pain was back again, the barriers were coming up, holding back the memories.

'Is that where you met your husband?'

She jerked her head up, appalled that he had somehow sensed her vulnerability, and resenting the intrusion. 'Yes, that's where I met Steve. He . . . he was a far better artist than I could ever have hoped to be.' Her fingers trailed over the surface of the desk, then went to her mouth, feeling it tremble. 'He was a perfectionist. I wasn't. I . . . After a while, one of my tutors introduced me to design and fabrics, and it was like a whole new world opening up. Suddenly I knew what I wanted to do.' She turned to look at him. 'I suppose that sounds crazy.'

He watched the conflicting emotions race across her face. 'Why should it? There's nothing wrong with knowing what you want and going all out to get it.'

Her chin jerked upwards. 'So why is it that when *you* say it, it sounds so . . . ruthless?'

'I'm not responsible for what you think of me, Kate.' There was a moment's taut silence. 'So you went straight from college into the business?'

Her gaze met his, then fell evasively. 'No, as a matter of fact, I got a job in an office. It was well paid and convenient.'

'Convenient for what, for God's sake?' He sounded

angry, and she felt confused by it. 'If you had a talent, why not use it instead of taking an easy option?'

'For the best of reasons, Mr Redmond.' She flushed, sensing criticism. 'At least, it seemed so to me. Because I was young, because I was going to marry the man I loved and because we were building a life and a home together.'

'So you made the noble sacrifice, is that it?'

A tight knot of panic stuck in her throat. 'No, it wasn't like that at all.' And it hadn't been. There had never been any question of sacrifice between herself and Steve. The choice had been entirely hers. Her gaze fell. She felt vexed with herself for having revealed more of her inner feelings to this man than to anyone for a long time.

Something of her confusion must have showed, because when Luke spoke all trace of mockery had gone from his voice. 'Exactly how long were you married, before the accident, Kate?'

She swallowed hard. This was private territory, and she was beginning to feel angry. 'Almost . . . almost a year.'

'Sometimes it helps to talk, even to a stranger, Kate, and five years is one hell of a long time to bottle up so much grief.' Suddenly he was a lot closer. 'Dammit, life goes on! You can't shut yourself away and pretend it isn't happening.'

Kate's face went deathly pale. 'What I do with my private life is none of your business. And frankly, Mr Redmond, I don't care to discuss my marriage with you.' She gasped then as his hands caught her arms in a vice-like grip. His eyes glittered dangerously.

'What exactly is it you're afraid of, Kate?'

'I'm not afraid.'

'No?'

She closed her eyes and clenched her teeth as he drew her closer, relentlessly forcing her to stay. There was tension in the set of his jaw, the line of the sensuous mouth, as with slow deliberation, it closed over hers. Weakly she willed him not to, but if he was aware of her resistance he ignored it, and she drew in a ragged breath as he kissed her with a ruthlessness which sent a shock-wave running through her. Her hands pressed against the muscular hardness of his chest as she tried desperately to control the tide of emotions which swept through her. Then, even as she struggled against the vital, rugged maleness of him, excitement burst through her like a flame.

She dragged herself from his grasp, breathing hard, fighting the sense of shock which was sweeping over her. Nothing had prepared her for it, nor for the sensuality of her own body which, like a traitor, had made her respond, no matter how briefly. She evaded his outstretched hand, unaware of the stark misery in her eyes.

She was shaking as she backed away. 'No!' Her fingers pressed to her mouth, where the imprint of his lips still remained, but she needn't have worried, because he made no attempt to follow her.

'Now tell me you're not afraid,' he muttered throatily. 'Tell me now that you still love him, Kate.'

She closed her eyes, wishing her heart would stop reacting so crazily. 'You've no right . . .'

'Dreams make poor bedfellows, Kate. Isn't it time

you exchanged them for something more real, more alive?'

Angry colour darkened her cheeks. 'Am I to take that as an offer, Mr Redmond?'

Anger flashed momentarily into his eyes, then he swore softly and, to her surprise, he turned to sit at the desk, from where he studied her with a contempt which took her breath away. 'I will admit the idea holds a certain attraction, but to put it bluntly, Mrs Langley, I prefer my women to be flesh and blood.'

'To go to bed with you, you mean?' Her eyes blazed. At that moment she hated him more than ever; he had opened a raw wound and seemed to be enjoying her pain. 'I'll bet that's how you usually do business.'

His expression didn't change, yet the sarcasm in his voice was barely contained. 'I'm a normal man with normal appetites. I work hard and I play equally hard. And while I'm willing to confess I do find you physically attractive,' his gaze raked her with an arrogance which seemed to strip her naked and left her gasping, 'I don't have to buy my entertainment.' He glanced at the gold watch he wore. 'And now I have some work to do, so unless there's anything specific you wish to discuss . . .'

Kate stared at him in total disbelief, her brain registering the cruelty and the complete lack of feeling with which he had delivered it. She felt the tears well up in her eyes, and had to swallow convulsively before she could speak. 'Just like that?'

He frowned, barely glancing up. 'I'd say the next move is definitely up to you. You know where the door is, or was there something else?' He sat appraising her with a studied arrogance which held her rooted to the spot, and for several heart-stopping seconds Kate actually found herself wondering what he would say . . . or do, if she said yes, there was something else. Sanity returned, and with it anger.

'Why, you—you bas——'

'I wouldn't if I were you, Kate,' he drawled in a voice cold with fury. 'In the first place, it isn't true. In the second, I might decide to exact my revenge, and somehow I don't think you're ready for that.'

She stared at him, and was exasperated to see the merest suspicion of a smile lurking in the dark eyes, but she refused to be fooled by it. Luke Redmond was completely unscrupulous and perfectly capable of carrying out his threat. Her fists clenched and unclenched. If it wasn't for the fact that she needed him—strictly in a business sense, of course, she told herself quickly—nothing would have prevented her from walking out there and then. As it was, she swallowed hard.

'I'm sorry. That was unforgivable.'

'I've been called worse,' he said blandly, 'by people who soon learned better.'

Kate shivered, believing it. It was difficult to imagine anyone getting the better of Luke Redmond and living to tell the tale! She forced herself to meet his gaze directly. 'I don't think I like the way you do business, Mr Redmond.' She reached for her bag, annoyed to find that she was still shaking. 'My partner and I invested a lot of time and effort into that contract for Halliday's. Presumably you, or Poseidon have their own ideas. Where does that leave me?' She frowned. 'I realise it would be foolish of me to expect you to behave honourably. I doubt if you even know the meaning of the word, and I'm certainly not prepared to get it at any price, especially not *your* price.'

He didn't blink an eyelid as he rose to his feet. 'One thing I've never done is to mix business with pleasure, Kate. As to my "price", as you put it, aren't you rather flattering yourself?'

She eyed him warily. 'I don't see . . .'

'No?' He raised one dark eyebrow. 'With all those other women lining up just for the chance to share my bed, I'm not at all sure when I'd get round to you.'

Kate blushed scarlet as she turned on her heel and headed for the door. He was insufferable! Worse, he was actually daring to laugh at her. She paused, turning to fix him with a sugary smile. 'Well, please don't trouble on my account, Mr Redmond. I'd hate to die of boredom while I wait.'

His lips twitched. 'Oh, well, if you're that desperate, I could make a real effort, just for you, Kate.'

With a muffled scream of exasperation she wrenched open the door, threw him a last look of loathing and marched out. 'Goodbye, Mr Redmond. It has definitely *not* been a pleasure.'

This time, he laughed aloud. 'Give it time, Kate. It *will* be, I promise you. I'll be in touch. There's still the little matter of a contract.'

She didn't even bother to answer. She was too angry and far too confused by emotions she had no intention of recognising. It was a long time since any man had roused anything more than indifference in her, and that was the way she preferred to keep it. Luke Redmond was the kind of experience she could well do without. As for seeing him again, that would never happen as far as she was concerned. Memories were far safer.

CHAPTER THREE

THE phone was already ringing insistently when Kate walked into the office next morning. There was nothing at all unusual about it. Unless she came in through the front entrance, Jenny, their receptionist-cum-secretary-cum-general-Girl-Friday, wouldn't know whether she had a rived or not, and would automatically put calls through.

Today, however, for some totally illogical reason, the sound of its ringing brought a rush of panic which held Kate frozen in the doorway, her throat dry as she stood waiting for it to stop. Only when it eventually fell silent, as Jenny automatically intercepted the call, could she bring herself to walk into the office where, having hung up her jacket, she sat at the desk and took several deep breaths before flipping the switch on the intercom.

'Yes, Mrs Langley?'

'Don't put any calls through to me until further notice, please, Jenny. If anything urgent crops up, take a message and say I'll get back to whoever it is, will you?'

'Yes, of course, Mrs Langley.'

'Thanks, Jenny. By the way . . . I just got in as the phone stopped ringing.' She bit her lip, despising herself for the lie. 'I don't suppose you know who it was?'

'Oh, yes, that was Mr Forrest, Mrs Langley. Would you like me to get him back for you?'

For a second Kate almost laughed at her groundless fears, as a surge of relief ran through her. 'Yes, please, Jenny. Do that now, will you? Then no more calls, no matter who. Understood?'

'Don't worry, I'll see to it, Mrs Langley.'

Kate sat back, aware that her hands were still shaking. It was sheer cowardice, she knew, but the mere thought of Luke Redmond carrying out his threat was more than she felt able to handle right now. Not that she seriously imagined for one minute he really would get in touch, she told herself, but she wasn't taking any chances. He would soon give up, when he learned that his domineering tactics didn't get him anywhere.

The intercom buzzed, making her heart leap. 'Yes, Jenny?'

'I have Mr Forrest on the line for you, Mrs Langley.'

She had to clear her throat before her voice could come out. 'Put him through.'

Mike's voice, familiar and tense, sounded in her ears. She smiled to herself, equilibrum restored. She listened, drawing a batch of typed letters towards her, which were awaiting her signature. Frowning, she delved into a drawer for a pen.

'Mike, I've already said I don't blame you. No, I don't feel at all bitter. I realise you had no choice . . .' She frowned impatiently, tucking the receiver under her chin as she flipped through a book of fabrics. 'Yes, yes, I know your hands were tied. I appreciate that you did what you had to do. It was good of you to try and help.'

Kate's partner, Sue Ross, had tiptoed in to put a stack of files on her desk, and was on her way out when Kate gestured, mouthing at her to stay. 'Yes, Mike, I'd really like to have dinner with you one evening, but not this week. No, no, I'm not annoyed, but we do have a lot of work on. Yes, that would be fine. Give me a call then. Yes, I'll look forward to it.' She put the phone down, sighing heavily.

'I take it that was Mike?' Sue perched her jean-clad bottom on the desk. 'Is he giving you trouble?'

'Not Mike, just his conscience.' Kate pushed the fabrics away, sighing ruefully. 'Lord, what a mess! I've explained that we don't hold him personally responsible. On the contrary—God knows, without him we'd probably have been kept in the dark a whole lot longer.'

'You obviously haven't seen this.' Sue dropped several editions of the daily papers on to the desk. 'It's all in there. Greek-based international hotel consortium take over failing British company.' She turned the pages of one paper, folding it in half. 'There's a picture of the new managing director. He's quite a dish, too. Wow, just imagine that combination! All that power, and lots of lovely loot too, and he can't be a day over thirty-five. What do you reckon?'

Kate stared at the unsmiling picture of Luke Redmond and felt her pulse quicken irrationally. Poor quality though the photograph was, there could be no mistaking those arrogant looks, the tanned face, dark eyes and sensual mouth which, even from the page, seemed to mock her. She pushed the paper aside. 'I really don't know. Frankly, he's not my type.'

'The trouble with you,' Sue eyed her sadly, 'is that you're judging all men by Steve.' She saw the faint flush gather in her friend's cheeks, and deliberately chose to ignore it. 'My guess is you're scared you might meet someone who *is* your type, so you freeze them all out, just to be on the safe side. And don't bother telling me to mind my own business, I've heard it before. I just happen to think it's a hell of a waste, that's all.'

Kate pressed a hand to her temple. 'Please, Sue, don't. Not now.'

'All right, all right.' Her friend threw her a look of exasperation. 'But I've known you for a long time, and all I want is to see you making some effort to live again. It makes me so damned angry to see you wasting yourself, filling your life with nothing but work, especially when there are gorgeous creatures like this around for the picking.'

Kate's eyes flashed a warning. 'Right now, my work is all I want. I don't need anything else. Certainly, I don't need another man in my life, so can we just drop the subject?' She pulled a folder from a stack of files. 'Have you managed to come up with any suitable brass fittings for that restaurant commission yet?'

'Nothing that really fits the bill.' Sue took the hint and changed the subject. 'In fact, I think we're going to have to get them specially made.'

'Isn't that going to increase the cost?'

'Not as far as I can tell, or at least only marginally,

and we have to weigh that against giving the customer what he wants as well as delivering on time. I've made some approaches to a small firm who've come up with some designs.' Sue reached for her briefcase and came out with a large envelope. 'Here, take a look at these.' She spread the drawings out on the desk, leaning over them with a frown of concentration. 'These are some of the ideas they've actually come up with and produced so far. Not their whole range, by any means, but I'm pretty impressed.'

Kate studied them, tapping a pen against her lip as she turned from one design to another. 'Mmm, I must admit they do look good, but this is only on paper. Have you seen some actual examples of finished articles?'

'Yes, I checked pretty thoroughly, and I'd say we can count on them.'

'What do you know about the company itself?'

'As yet it's pretty small, started out much as we did, more or less on a wing and a prayer, but they're beginning to build up quite a reputation, based on good, solid workmanship and reliability. This is a price list.'

Kate scanned it briefly. 'It looks good, and reasonably competitive.'

'It is,' Sue affirmed. 'In fact, if they come up with the goods this time, I reckon we could probably use them again. You know yourself how often we've wanted a small but specialised item which the bigger suppliers either can't or won't provide. Well, these people are quite happy to produce what we want. All we have to do is come up with the ideas.'

Kate sat back and noded. 'It sounds good. This isn't exactly a small order, though. We're asking for light fittings, decorative scrolling and . . . what else was it?'

'Powder-room fittings.'

'And they don't see any problems over delivery?'

'None at all.'

Kate shuffled through the papers again, considering them in silence for a moment. 'Well, in that case, let's take the risk and confirm a definite order.'

Sue grinned. 'I'll do that. I'm all for helping small enterprise along.'

'But what happens when small enterprise becomes big enterprise?'

'We'll probably have to start looking all over again. *C'est la vie*, as they say. How about some coffee?'

'I'd say it sounds like a brilliant idea.' Kate pressed the switch on the intercom. 'Jenny, can you bring some coffee in? Oh, and the morning post, if you've had a chance to go through it. By the way, have those wallpaper samples come in yet?'

'Yes, they have, Mrs Langley. I'll bring them in with me when I bring your coffee.'

'Thanks, Jen.' Kate reached across her desk for the batch of fabrics again, pushing them towards Sue. 'I'm still not happy about that green layout we did for the hairdressing salon.'

Sue held two shades together, tilting her head on one side as she considered them. 'I thought it was what the owners wanted? Not my choice, I must admit, but ours is not to reason why if they listen to our advice and then decide to reject it.'

'I don't think they actually *did* reject it. They

weren't too decisive about anything, and I reckon we should press them gently towards something a little less harsh, bearing in mind that, with the lights on, clients are going to take one look in the mirrors and get a nasty shock when they see themselves looking slightly off colour.'

Sue thumbed through the fabrics. 'Have you checked to see that that's what happens?'

'Believe me, it does, and green does nothing for my complexion!'

'So, any alternative suggestions?'

'Something warmer?'

'Pink?'

'Maybe. Different shades of pink. We'll do a mock-up. We can always use plants and greenery to bring in the contrasts. Mirrors give an illusion of added space, and we can tone floor coverings and chairs to wash-basins like this.'

Heads together, they moved cut-out scale segments on a large, transparent plastic sheet, bringing down layers of added colour and varying arrangements until the desired effect was reached.

'I'd say that was it.'

Kate smiled. 'I think you're right. Ah, coffee!'

Sue cleared a space on the desk as Jenny came in with a tray of coffee and the morning's post. 'Biscuits, too! Jen, you're an angel.'

The teenager blushed. 'Just don't blame me when you get a black mark at your diet class, that's all. Oh, Mrs Langley, I know you said not to put any calls through, but one caller in particular has been very persistent. I did explain that you were engaged, and asked if I could take a message, but he refused. He keeps ringing back and asking to speak to you, in person.'

Kate's hand shook as she poured coffee, exclaiming crossly as she spilled some into the saucer. 'Did he leave a name, or a number?'

Jenny frowned. 'Well, no, not exactly. That is——' she screwed up her face apologetically '—he just said that you'd know who it was, and that he doesn't give up that easily. I'm sorry if that doesn't make any sense. I did try.'

Kate's green eyes held a hint of panic. 'That's all right, Jenny, I know you did and I do understand.' She carefully avoided Sue's curious glance as she handed her her coffee.

'So what shall I say if . . . when he rings back again?'

There were several things which sprang instantly to Kate's mind, but she suppressed a desire to voice them aloud. 'Just tell him the same as before, please, Jenny—that I'm extremely busy and can't be disturbed.'

This time, the girl's face flamed with colour. 'Actually, I did tell him that, Mrs Langley, last time he called.' She bit her lower lip apprehensively.

'And what exactly did he say?' Kate asked he tersely.

'Well, he said . . . he said, "Tell her she can fool herself but she can't fool me." And then he put the phone down.'

'Oh, did he, indeed?' Kate's face burned scarlet with mortification, and Sue choked over her coffee.

'Do I take it that this is the forceful Mr Redmond? If so, you certainly have to give him full marks for persistence.'

Kate's mouth compressed ominously. 'I wouldn't give him full marks for anything except pig-headedness. Next time he calls, Jenny, tell him I'm out and won't be back for several days. I may even be leaving the country.'

'Yes, Mrs Langley.' Jenny left the office, and Sue half sat on the desk, her hands clasped round the mug of coffee.

'You know,' she said wryly, 'sooner or later you're going to have to talk to him. Like it or not, a deal with Poseidon could open a lot of doors.'

Kate threw her a slanting glance. 'The problem is—is *he* going to be behind each one?' Taking her coffee, she went to stand at the window, schooling her features to remain calm, while inside her emotions were in turmoil. For some reason she couldn't or didn't want to understand, Luke Redmond seemed to offer a threat. It had taken her five years, five long, often desperate years, to get her life back into some sort of order after Steve had died.

She shivered now as the pain of carefully submerged memories began bubbling up to the surface. Her work, setting up the business, had helped. She had deliberately driven herself hard, almost to the point at one stage where her friends had feared she was heading for a nervous breakdown. They had all put it down to the accident, the shock of hearing that Steve had been killed outright in the car that night when he had apparently skidded off the road and hit a tree. But there was more to it than that, Kate knew. Much more. Things she could never bring herself to talk about, not even to Sue, who has become her closest friend and ally.

And now, just when it seemed she had begun to get things back into some sort of perspective, see some purpose in what she was doing, Luke Redmond had somehow managed to force a tiny gap in all her carefully erected barriers. Well, barriers could be rebuilt, and she had no intention of allowing him to encroach any further.

'I don't think we can afford that kind of prestige,' she said crossly. 'We don't need Luke Redmond.'

Sue flung her a look of amusement. 'Isn't there just a chance you're making a somewhat personal judgement here? Obviously he doesn't share your opinion, so perhaps you made more of an impression than you think.'

Kate stirred her coffee with unnecessary briskness. She had asked herself that same question, too, and the conclusions she came to were so completely illogical that she had discarded them almost as quickly as they rose. 'The only thing likely to make any impression on Mr Redmond's thick hide would be a ten-ton rhino at full gallop!' And even then came the suspicion that he would deal with it without as much as a flicker of the dark eyelashes. Her eyes flared and she banged her cup down decisively. 'Shall we drop the subject and get back to work? I thought you wanted us both to call in at the suppliers this afternoon?'

'It's OK, I'll do it.' One look at the lines of strain in her friend's face pursuaded Sue to let the matter drop, though not without a deep sense of regret for what she considered to be a terrible waste of a young life.

She had known Steve Langley as long as she had known Kate, and she hadn't liked what she had known, but had wisely kept her own counsel. She had watched their romance grow, had been chief bridesmaid at their wedding. And it had been no consolation to discover that, even within the first weeks, the vague fears she had felt were already beginning to be proved correct. She hadn't known the circumstances, and Kate had never talked about it, but she had seen her friend change slowly from a lively, outgoing person to someone quiet and withdrawn. And yet, for some reason even she couldn't fathom, Steve's sudden and tragic death had only seemed to trap Kate in a cage of guilt from which she seemed incapable—or unwilling—or break free.

'I've got some letters to go in this evening's post. I'd better go and get myself organised.' Sue's smiling amber eyes hid her real concern as she waved and left the office.

For the rest of the day, Kate forced herself to concentrate with such intensity on her work that, by the time she finally reached for her coat and bag, her neck muscles were stiff with tension.

Going through to the outer office, she dropped a pile of letters on to the desk. 'These are all signed, Jenny. I'm going home early. I think I must have a migraine coming on.'

Jenny was already rising from behind her desk. 'You do look pale. Can I get you anything, Mrs Langley? Some aspirin?'

Kate shook her head, and wished she hadn't, as a wave of pain increased until it was like a tight band.

'No, thanks, Jen. I have some medication at home. I'll take some as soon as I get in, and have an early night.' She looked at her watch and had difficulty focusing on its tiny face. 'Why don't you go off yourself? There's nothing that can't wait till tomorrow, is there? And I dare say you have a date.'

Jen ran her eyes over the desk. 'Well, yes, I do, as a matter of fact. I'm going to the theatre. Thanks, Mrs Langley.'

Kate managed a smile. 'Call me Kate, will you? Mrs Langley sounds horribly formal.'

'If you're sure you don't mind.' Jen smiled shyly. 'Well, thanks and goodnight then, Kate. I hope you feel better in the morning.'

Climbing into her car, and driving home through eternal traffic jams and the heat which now held a hint of thunder, Kate nursed a growing suspicion that, if present signs were anything to go by, this was one migraine she wasn't going to be able to sleep off.

The flat at least was cool and welcoming. Her actions purely automatic, she went through the rooms, drawing curtains, shutting out the light before going to run a bath. Having made coffee, she swallowed two of the strong pain-killers prescribed by her doctor. With a bit of luck, they would make the symptoms more bearable and she would sleep. Lying awake at night was one of the things she had come to dread, though there were times when even that was preferable to the nightmares which came when she did manage to sleep.

Going into the bedroom, Kate stripped off her clothes and stood naked in front of the mirror as she slipped her arms into the sleeves of a satin robe. Without any sense of false modesty, she knew she had a good figure. Admittedly, she was thinner now than five years ago, but the honing of a little excess flesh was all to the good.

The shock came when she stared at features scarcely recognisable as her own. Her eyes were like huge, green, pain-filled smudges in the pale face. Her mouth was trembling with distress and, even as she watched, hot tears welled up and began to fall down her cheeks. Yet the strange thing was that she didn't know why she was crying, nor for whom. She hadn't even wept when Steve had been killed. They had said it was delayed shock, but surely five years was too long?

Dashing the tears away, Kate made for the bathroom. She had shed her robe and was about to step into the steaming, perfumed water when the doorbell rang. Groaning inwardly, she told herself she would ignore it. Whoever it was would soon give up and go away.

Sighing, she eased herself into the scented bubbles and lay back, closing her eyes to block out the pain which was tightening like a steel band round her forehead.

The doorbell rang again, longer and more insistently this time, as if the caller was becoming angry. Kate's fist slammed with annoyance against the bath as she dragged herself out of the water again, and shrugged the robe over her wet body. Whoever it was had better have a good reason . . .

She wrenched open the door, and felt the colour flood into her cheeks as she stared in disbelief at the figure standing there.

'You!' For several seconds, shock held her rigid, as Luke Redmond's gaze swept with slow appreciation over her body, the dark eyes taking in every curve, every outline which, she realised, blushing hotly, must be visible beneath the damp robe. Involuntarily, she pulled it more securely around her in a jerky movement, her flush deepening as his mouth curved with mocking laughter.

'Expecting someone, Kate?'

For a moment, confusion furrowed her brow and then, as realisation dawned, she moved quickly, slamming the door to a close, except that it didn't. With seemingly no effort at all, Like Redmond was in the flat, and it was he who closed the door, watching as she backed away.

The look of amusement was gone from the dark eyes, to be replaced by glittering impatience now as he went towards her. 'I'd like to think that this is all for me,' he said, huskily, as in one subtle movement he caught the tie which should have held her robe together, and with slow deliberation drew Kate, trembling, towards him.

Her startled gaze widened. 'What are *you* doing here? What do you want?'

His dark gaze roamed slowly over her face. 'You've been avoiding me, Kate.'

She wrenched herself from his grasp. 'What makes you think I'd do that, Mr Redmond?'

'*Luke,*' he said tersely. 'As to why, I can't imagine, especially as it's in your interests to talk to me.'

'We are talking about my business interests, of

course?'

'I'm always prepared to be flexible.' There was a glint of mockery in his eyes. 'I think what I have to offer will be of interest.'

Her green eyes flashed angrily. 'Look, I've had a hard day, I'm tired and I have a splitting headache, so what exactly is it that you want?'

'I thought I'd already made myself pretty clear on that issue, Kate,' said softly. 'That aside, you've been deliberately refusing to answer my calls. I'd like to know why, when we still have unfinished business to discuss.'

'I've already explained,' she snapped. 'I was busy.' His close proximity, and the heady scent of his aftershave, were having a strangely disturbing effect on her nerves. 'You could have left a message with my secretary.'

His mouth twisted derisively. 'I don't deal with secretaries, Kate. As a matter of interest, would you have answered anyway?'

She threw him a sharp look before her gaze fell. Her head was throbbing, and as her fingers probed the spot she was surprised to discover that her hands were actually shaking. 'I really don't think there would be much point, do you, Mr Redmond? I think we said all there was to say.'

He swore softly, his hand reaching out to encircle her wrist in a vice-like grip. 'The name's Luke, damn you—why don't you use it?'

Kate could feel his body heat as he pulled her gently, yet with surprising force, towards him. She licked her dry lips, then threw him a deliberately provocative smile.

'As you wish. After all, what's in a name—Luke?'

'A great deal when *you* say it, Kate. I like the sound of it.'

With a ragged breath, she released her hand from his grasp. 'As I said, I didn't see much point.'

He frowned. 'I told you I'd be in touch.'

'Oh, I'm sorry!' She laughed bitterly. 'I was under the impression that was a threat rather than a statement, and I don't respond to threats.'

In a single, effortless movement, he caught her, and she gasped as she found herself jerked against his taut, muscular frame. 'I wonder just what you *do* respond to, Kate.' His eyes glittered dangerously. 'Suppose we find out.'

Hot colour flooded her cheeks, and her lips parted in a furious protest, which died as his mouth captured hers in a slow, utterly ruthless kiss which needed no force to make her gasp at the sheer sensuality of it. She was too stunned to retaliate or resist. As if he sensed it, Luke groaned softly, drawing her closer still as his hand moved lightly against her hair, her cheeks and then the soft mounds of her breasts.

A flame of passion so unexpected and intense ran through her that she gasped involuntarily as his lips moved lower and lower still, finding spots of pleasure she hadn't known had existed until now.

He lowered her to the sofa and went down with her, his hands pushing aside the soft fabric of the thin robe. 'Dear God!' he rasped. 'You're even more beautiful than I imagined.'

A ragged protest was silenced again as his mouth

closed more hungrily over hers, his fingers tracing her spine, the lines of her breast, her waist—his mouth moving slowly to her stomach.

She gave a choking cry as each deliberately calculated movement sent a shaft of aching, exquisite desire searing through her. Her fingers entwined in his dark hair as her body arched towards her.

She could feel the hard strength of his thighs against her legs, bruising her flesh in his urgency.

'I want you,' he moaned huskily. 'I want to make love to you as much as you want me to.'

'No!' The strangled cry of protest came as the sound of his voice brought her brutally back to reality.

'Yes, Kate.' His hands held her prisoner. 'You *do* want me.'

In a wave of humiliation, she realised that her own fingers had torn open the buttons of his shirt, that she would have gone on to . . . to what? The thought was too mortifying to consider. 'No!'

Summoning every ounce of her strength, Kate pushed him away, her cheeks burning as she pulled the robe over her nakedness.

Easing himself back, he stared at her with raw agony. 'What's wrong, Kate? What is it?'

She shook her head, eyes tightly shut in an attempt to hold back the tears. For a few brief seconds she had *wanted* him to make love to her. Heart thudding, she struggled to regain control of her emotions.

He shifted his weight above her. 'You're lying, Kate. I don't know why, but you're lying.'

She couldn't bring herself to look at him as she pushed him away. Getting up from the sofa, she hugged the robe protectively about her, even though it was too late, he already knew everything about her body. More than she knew, or had imagined herself.

For a second, blind panic consumed her, and she had to clench her fists to prevent herself from shaking. For a while he had actually made her forget the vow she had made to herself that it could never happen again. Falling in love brought nothing but heartache, and she had already had more than her fair share of that. But what she had failed to take into account was that she would meet someone like Luke Redmond, and the fact that her own body might betray her.

'Kate, in God's name, what is it?'

He was on his feet, re-fastening his shirt as he came towards her, but she warded him off.

'Don't! Please, don't touch me.'

Luke stopped in his tracks, his expression grim, but he made no attempt to move closer. The turmoil in her eyes seemed warning enough that if he did she would run.

'I wouldn't hurt you. You must know that?'

She stared at him through a haze of pain as her head seemed to be gripped by a band of steel. 'Let's just forget it happened. It certainly won't ever again.'

He stood motionless, his eyes darkened with pain and confusion. 'Do you really still love him that much?'

For an instant, Kate stared at him uncomprehendingly, then she drew a ragged breath. He assumed she had rejected him because she was still clinging to her memories of Steve, yet the irony of the situation was that it was Steve himself who had gradually killed any remaining feelings of love she might have had. In the months before his death he had changed so much that the only emotions he had roused in her were fear and pity, and finally intense sadness for what he had become. But Luke Redmond didn't know that, and that, she realised triumphantly, was her best, her only defence against him.

Her gaze rose to meet his. 'I suggest you draw your own conclusions and then forget what just happened, just as I intend doing.' She turned away.

'And if I don't want to forget?' He caught her, pulling her roughly to face him.

She swallowed hard. 'I'm afraid you don't have any choice.' She focused her gaze on him, aware of the steel strength of his body against hers. She broke away. Men like Luke Redmond were safer kept at arm's length. 'I told you, I'm not interested.'

'Correction,' he said tersely. 'I think I've just proved that to be incorrect, to both our satisfaction, whether or not you care to admit it. So I won't accept that you still love your husband, because I don't believe it.'

Her heart lurched in sudden panic. 'My feelings for Steve have nothing to do with you.'

'Oh, I'd say they have a great deal to do with me, Kate. As you're beginning to realise, I'm flesh and blood, and no memory in the world can make you feel the way you did just now.'

Her cheeks blazed scarlet. 'It won't happen again, Mr Redmond, that's a promise. Just put it down to a moment of irrational weakness.'

His mouth twisted derisively. 'Call it what you like, Kate, but don't make promises that you can't and I certainly don't intend to keep.'

She gasped at the blatant threat contained in the words, then moved quickly to the door, jerking it open. 'I think you'd better leave. You got what you came for.'

His eyes scanned her pale face, moving to her body, which was barely concealed by the thin robe, and he smiled mockingly. 'I wouldn't say that, Kate. As a matter of fact——' he took an envelope from his inner jacket pocket and tossed it on to the coffee table '—this is the real reason I came. I really did mean to talk business—I told you I had your interests at heart. Perhaps you'd better read that through.'

'What is it?' Kate dragged her gaze warily from his face to the envelope.

'Why not read it? It's a draft report drawn up by our legal and technical experts on hotel and conference facilities for Poseidon UK.

'They didn't lose any time, did they?' she said drily.

'We don't pay them to.'

'Oh, no.' Her eyes flashed. 'And of course everyone has a price, is that it?'

He raised an eyebrow. 'If it is, I'd be interested to know yours.'

Her heart thudded erratically. He was deliberately challenging her, and her blood boiled at his arrogance. 'Whatever it is, you certainly couldn't meet it.' She glanced at the envelope. 'What makes you think I'd be interested in those?'

'I don't think you'll be able to resist the challenge.'

'Some are remarkably easy to resist, Mr Redmond.'

His mouth curved with laughter, 'Not this one, Kate. Look through the plans, think about it, and we can discuss your ideas over lunch tomorrow. I'll pick you up at one o'clock.'

She threw him a scathing glance. 'Please don't bother. It would be a waste of your time and mine, especially as we'd have nothing to discuss.'

'That's fine by me,' he smiled. 'No business talk— shall I make it twelve-thirty?'

'I'm on a diet,' she insisted firmly, then frowned as the phone rang. So much for an early night, she thought. Who on earth could it be? 'You can show yourself out, I take it?' She glared at Luke, picking up the telephone and turning her back deliberately.

'I'll wait till you've finished,' he drawled softly. 'I'd hate to leave on an indecisive note.'

Kate scowled heavily, uncovering the phone's mouthpiece. 'Yes?' she snapped.

'Hello, Kate. It's Mike. I haven't called at a bad time, have I?'

'Mike! No, no, of course you haven't called at a bad time.' Her face lit with pleasure, oblivious to the sudden look of anger which swept Luke's features.

'You sound a little tense. I'm sorry if I'm interrupting anything.'

'You're not interrupting a thing.' She glanced defiantly at Luke, and couldn't surpress a hint of mischief. 'As a matter of fact, I was feeling bored. I've promised myself an early night with a good book.' She gasped as Luke's arm came round her waist, and he spoke with cool deliberation against her ear.

'You won't be needing your book, darling, not if I have anything to say in the matter.'

Kate covered the mouthpiece quickly, throwing him a look of fury, conscious of the look of quiet laughter in his eyes. He had done it deliberately, knowing that Mike would hear. Her cheeks blazed as she picked the phone up and moved as far away as possible.

Mike sounded distinctly flustered, and . . . was there a hint of jealousy in his voice, too? 'I *have* interrupted something, haven't I? I didn't realise you'd have anyone with you.'

'Don't be silly, Mike!' she snapped peevishly. 'I told you, it's nothing . . . no one important.'

There was a momentary pause. 'Actually, I rang to ask if you'd have lunch with me tomorrow. I still feel guilty about what happened and I'd like a chance to explain.'

'There's really no need.'

'Well, I'd still like to put the record straight. Things were more or less taken out of my hands, you know. Redmond isn't the sort of man to let anything or anyone stand in the way. I'd avoid him like the plague if I were you.'

Kate glanced at Luke, and had to suppress the uncanny feeling that he could hear every word Mike said. 'That sounds like pretty good advice, and about lunch tomorrow—it's a lovely idea. I'd like it very much.' She glared directly at Luke, then shivered as the rugged features darkened angrily. 'I'm sure we'll have a lot to talk about.' She almost winced to hear the deliberately provocative note in her own voice, but she had no intention of allowing herself to be intimidated—or anything else—by Luke Redmond. 'Till tomorrow, then. Same place as usual.

She rang off, studiously avoiding the expression in Luke's eyes, yet his anger was tangible, reaching out to her so that she shivered again, hugging her arms about her own body in a self-protective embrace.

His eyes glittered as he studied her for a long moment, during which her body tensed as if it recognised a threat in his mere physical nearness.

She licked her lips nervously, aware of the sheer animal magnetism of him, and felt the stirrings of betrayal in her own body again. He moved closer, almost as if he had sensed her silently willing him not to. He pulled her roughly against him, and her head went back as his closeness and her own body's response made a mockery of her tiny act of defiance.

'You won't win, you know,' he insisted, cupping her face, holding it captive as his mouth played provocatively over hers, teasing, biting, drawing a groan from her as she tried to resist the sensuality of this man.

His body was taut, she could sense the power of him as she curved against him. His thumbs traced the contours of her cheeks, then her lips. She closed her eyes tightly, refusing to let him see the effect he was having on her, but he laughed softly and she gasped again as his hand suddenly covered her breast, where the nipple rose at his touch, like a flower bursting into bloom. As her lips parted in protest, his kiss silenced her again, muffling her tiny sob of frustration.

'So my company bores you, does it, Kate?' he

murmured throatily. 'Strange.' His hand moved to the soft silkiness of her back, drawing her closer as she uttered a protest. 'That isn't the impression I get.'

'Please, I . . .'

'Oh, I intend to, Kate, but it will be a mutual pleasure, I promise.'

She gasped then, as his knee gently forced her legs apart. 'No!'

'Yes, Kate. Yes.' His voice was muffled by her hair as he kissed her throat. 'I want you, and you want me. Say it, damn you, admit it!'

His hand flicked the thin robe open, exposing her shoulders and breasts. It moved slowly, insidiously over her back and thighs, and lower still, until she cried out, her body arching against the taut throbbing of his thighs.

'Say it,' he commanded, brutally silencing her inarticulate moans of protest with his lips. 'Say, "I want you Luke."'

She was fighting him and the effect he was having upon her with every ounce of strength she possessed. The knowledge that he could rouse her to the point where she forgot all sanity, until her body throbbed beneath the sensual pleasure his hands gave, sent quivers of both desire and fear shuddering through her body. Yes, she had no doubt he *wanted* her, and hadn't he warned her that sooner or later he always got what he wanted?

She tore her mouth from his. How many women had he made love to like this? How many had he walked away from? Her breath came in sharp, uneven gasps as she pushed him away.

'No, it's not true.'

His head rose and she saw the look of anguished disbelief in his eyes. 'You're lying!'

She shook her head, knowing that what he said was true, but she couldn't go through the pain and disillusionment of loving and losing someone all over again.

He released her so abruptly that she staggered and had to hold on to a chair for support. She was breathing hard, and could feel the burning in her cheeks as he looked at her, his expression fierce.

'I don't think you have any idea what you do to me. If you did, you wouldn't play such dangerous games.'

Shaken by the discovery, she managed to walk to the door and held it open. 'Goodnight, Mr Redmond. In case you've forgotten, you came here uninvited and I've asked you several times to leave.'

He paused at the door. 'One of these days, I'll break through those defences of yours, Kate, so you'd better watch out.'

She swallowed hard. 'Is that another threat?'

'No, that's a promise,' he said softly. 'Don't forget to look through those plans. Sleep tight and sweet dreams. I'll be in touch.'

She made no attempt to answer. Closing the door firmly behind him, she locked it and stood for a moment, breathing deeply. Luke Redmond was everything she despised—arrogant, domineering and completely ruthless. The kind of man who believed that simply because he wanted something it had to happen, and right now he wanted her. Well, her defences were far too strongly built to be in any danger from a man like that.

CHAPTER FOUR

AFTER he had gone, Kate sat for a long time, hunched in front of the glow from the electric fire, sipping at her coffee. The bath water had long since gone cold and, more frustratingly, she no longer felt in the least bit tired. Quite the reverse, she realised with a sense of irritation. Her brain seemed to have sprung to life, even the headache had gone, and suddenly the last thing she wanted was to go to bed.

Hugging the robe more closely around her, she padded over to the TV set, watched it flicker into life, and gave a slight grimmce of distaste as she recognised a well-known soap. She went from one channel to another, before finally giving up and switching it off again.

Outside, the late summer sky was just darkening. She went through the flat, straightening ornaments and plumping cushions in an attempt to keep herself occupied. She moved a magazine from the coffee table and, in doing so, her hand brushed against the envelope Luke had dropped there. She pushed it aside and carried her empty cup to the kitchen, where she washed and dried it and put it away.

As she returned to the lounge, however, her gaze was drawn again to the envelope. After all, she asked herself, what possible harm could it do just to read through it? As a designer, she felt a sneaking urge to discover just what Luke Redmond's experts had come up with, to see whether her own ideas corresponded; not that it was likely, since her views and Luke's seemed to be poles apart on everything.

Sitting on the sofa, she tucked her legs up beside her and began to read, quickly at first, barely scanning the pages to get an outline of what was typed there. But gradually she found herself going back to study at greater length. A frown furrowed her brow, and she tugged at her lower lip as she became absorbed in facts and figures. It was all there—costings, a layout of proposals, the pros and cons of each varying scheme, the legal aspects and a preliminary floor plan, which to the untrained eye would have meant little but, as she turned the pages, Kate could feel the stirrings of excitement in her stomach.

Without even thinking about it, she reached for a pen and sketch-pad and began making notes. Ideas fell over themselves, she even scribbled out her own costings, until with a sudden cry of angry frustration she flung them down and went to stare out of the window into now total drakness. After all, what was the point?

The bitter irony of it was that, if she accepted this job, she would also have to accept Luke Redmond as a controlling, all-consuming and far too dangerous intrusion into her life. Or was that precisely what he had counted on? That she wouldn't be able to resist? But to what purpose? Her green eyes widened with shock at a thought so fleeting that she barely recognised it, before it flickered through her mind and vanished.

She stood in the light from the one solitary lamp, her figure unconsciously graceful, her hair tumbled over her shoulders where he had disarranged it, seeming more golden in the light. Suddenly she felt exhausted, and was shocked when she looked at the clock to discover that it was well after midnight. Yet she still felt a reluctance to go to bed, until common sense reminded her that she had to get up and go to work in a few hours and, besides, she was safe now, if she discounted the knowledge that her body still pulsated from the skilful arousal which had left her feeling trapped yet strangely unsatisfied.

Slipping off her robe, Kate slid naked between the sheets and closed her eyes, but it was still a long time before she slept. She tossed and turned for what seemed an eternity before finally falling asleep just before dawn, only to discover that in her dreams she wasn't as safe from Luke Redmond as in reality. In her dreams her resistance seemed to fade, and when she was woken, gasping with shock, to the sound of the telephone ringing, her body was filmed with sweat, and the bruises, far from fading, seemed more real.

Kate fought her way out of the covers, groaning as she struggled to rid her drugged brain of the last remnants of sleep. She hadn't imagined it, the phone was definitely ringing. Her gaze flew to the clock, certain she must have overslept, only to gasp with angry disbelief as she saw it read seven o'clock. She reached for the phone, brushing the heavy mane of hair back as she lay back against the pillow, the receiver pressed against her ear.

'Hello.' Her voice came out thick and still heavy with sleep, and there was a momentary pause before the voice at the other end replied.

'Did I wake you from a nice dream, Kate?'

If she hadn't been properly awake before, she certainly was now as she sat up, hot colour flushing her cheeks. 'L—Luke? Wh——No.' She gritted her teeth on the lie, and thought she heard him laugh quietly at the other end of the phone. 'No, I've been awake for hours. I was just making coffee, as a matter of face.'

'You're not a very good liar, Kate,' he rasped. 'Don't be ashamed to admit you were dreaming of me. I only wish I'd been there to wake you in person. I'd have taken my time over it.'

She sat up, by now fully awake, and groped for the sheet, only to remind herself that she was being ridiculous. He coudn't possibly know that she was naked, or what she had dreamed. She moistened her dry lips, caught sight of herself in the mirror and was shocked to discover that her cheeks were flushed and her eyes brilliant.

'Kate, are you still there?' There was a faint hint of concern in his voice.

'Wh——Oh, yes, of course I'm still here,' she snapped, suddenly feeling cross. I take it you have a very good reason for wa . . . calling me so early, Mr Redmond?'

'It was Luke a moment ago, before you had time to remember to put the barriers up.'

She frowned, swallowing hard, as it seemed that

even from a distance he had the power to awaken her senses. 'I wasn't thinking,' she said briskly. 'You took me by surprise.'

'I must do it more often. In fact, I rather like the idea—of waking you up slowly, that is, of seeing the look of surprise—and pleasure in your eyes.'

'Then I'm afraid you'll have a long wait,' she said irritably, frightened by the way her body behaved as if it had a mind of its own, beyond her controlling, 'because to do that you would have to be . . .' She broke off, choking slightly as she realised what she had almost said.

'There beside you?' He said it for her, and she was glad he couldn't see the colour scorching into her face.

She got out of bed, shrugging herself into her robe. 'What exactly is it that you want?'

He made a slight sound which might have been laughter. 'You really want me to be specific?'

She had walked right into it. The knowledge made her give a brief, wry smile. She deliberately made her voice cool. 'Can we change the subject? I do have to get to work, so, unless you'd care to tell me your reason for calling at such an ungodly hour, I intend to take the course recommended to anyone receiving an obscene phone call.'

'I promise you there's nothing at all obscene about what I have in mind to do to you, Kate, and one day you'll realise that. You seem to be in need of some intense re-education.'

'Which you, as an expert, are no doubt willing to undertake?'

'But of course.' His voice was taut now. 'Making love is something to be learned and lingered over, Kate—if both parties are to enjoy it to the full.'

She drew a deep, controlling breath. 'I'll be sure to remember that, *when* I meet the right person. And now, if you will forgive me, I do have to get ready to go to work. I have a particularly busy day.'

'And a lunch date, of course.'

'Of course.' Her voice threw out a deliberate challenge as she sensed he was suddenly angry.

There was a momentary pause again, and this time she was the one to break it. 'Luke, are you still there?'

'Yes, I'm still here.' She could imagine the dark eyes glittering coldly. 'And you're right, I have a busy day ahead, too. Which is the reason I called so early. I appreciate that you can't make lunch, so I'll pick you up this evening for dinner—will seven-thirty be all right? Or would you prefer to make it a little later?'

Kate gasped, 'But we don't have a date for this evening! I don't . . .'

'You're right,' he said curtly, 'we don't. What I'm suggesting is strictly a business meeting. I take it you did read the report I left with you?'

'Well, yes, I did, but . . . I really . . .'

'Then I'd say we have a great deal to talk about. You must at least have formed an opinion, some ideas.'

Her mouth compressed. 'But I told you, I'm not interested.'

'You mean, you don't think you're capable of doing the job?'

'No!' The protest came sharply. 'I mean, yes, I consider myself perfectly capable, it's just that . . .'

'You're afraid of it.'

'No!'

'So what have you got to lose?' Quite a lot, she thought ruefully, as if he didn't know. Into the silence, he said, 'Can you really afford to turn it down?'

'What do you mean?'

'You must have weighed up the pros and cons, taken into account the kind of prestige not to say financial rewards an account like this could bring. Or perhaps you intend spending the rest of your life wasting your undoubted talents in a business which hardly does them, or you, justice, which is ticking along but will never make you a fortune.'

She was shaking with shock, her eyes blazing with anger. 'You've been checking up . . .'

'I'm running a business, Kate. I don't make mistakes, I certainly don't take chances.'

Her fists clenched and unclenched as she fought to bring herself under control. 'But isn't that precisely what you'd be doing with me, *if* I decided to do the designs?' She wished he was there so that she could see him, face to face, see the expression in his eyes. 'Why me? There must be dozens of other designers, all equally if not more qualified.' She frowned her confusion. 'There has to be a reason . . .'

'You're right, there is.' The lazily drawled words took her breath away.

'Then wh——'

'Can't you guess, Kate?'

Colour darkened her cheeks. She *could* guess. That

was the trouble. Her imagination ran riot. 'I don't think I care to,' she said weakly, and told herself she imagined his soft sigh of impatience.

'I'll pick you up for dinner tonight, then. Seven-thirty?'

She was glad he couldn't see her confusion. 'I . . .'

'Strictly business,' he said sharply. 'If that's the way you want it.' Was he mocking her? She couldn't tell without seeing his eyes, and then she was glad she couldn't, because that would mean he could see her, too. 'You'd be a fool not to, Kate.' Was there a hint of threat in the words?

'Why, what do you mean?'

He paused slightly. 'I would have thought it's obvious—if it gets about that you were considered for the job and someone else gets it, people might start putting two and two together and drawing their own conclusions.'

'But people couldn't possibly think that.'

'Who knows how people's minds work? If they once get the idea that you're not up to it . . .'

'But that's not true. You *know* it isn't.'

'I don't know any such thing. You haven't convinced *me* yet.'

Kate sat on the bed again, too stunned to take in the full implications of his words straight away. She swallowed hard. 'Why do I get the distinct feeling I'm being blackmailed?'

'I can't imagine.' His voice implied that he didn't care. 'I'll pick you up at seven-thirty. I've booked a table. By the way, don't forget you have a lunch date.'

Kate drew in an angry breath. 'Make it eight

o'clock,' she said perversely. 'I shall need the extra time to sharpen my claws.'

'Don't bother, Kate. Just come as you are—your sweet, loving, natural self.'

Kate slammed down the phone, but not before she was sure she had heard him laugh—or was it perhaps a cry of rage? Either way, she decided, hurrying to the bathroom to turn on the shower, Luke Redmond was lethal and, if she wanted to survive, she was going to have to start making a few rules of her own!

Kate stood in the doorway of the crowded wine bar, her gaze scanning the smoke-filled room until she saw Mike waving in her direction. She went towards him, a smile on her lips, completely unaware of the attractive figure she made in the cool linen skirt and matching jacket, and the jade-coloured shirt which gave a quite stunning and totally unwitting emphasis to her eyes.

Mike had already bought drinks. His own glass was empty, her glass of orange juice stood waiting. Mike knew her tastes, he didn't need to ask what she wanted. He kissed her cheek as he made way for her at the table.

'I was afraid you weren't going to make it.'

Kate settled into the seat, tucking her bag down by her feet, and drew a breath of relief. The traffic had been heavy and, despite appearances, she felt hot.

'I really am sorry, Mike. I know I'm horribly late, something cropped up. It was rather urgent, and by the time I tried to reach you, you'd already left the office.' She bit her lip, knowing that she could hardly tell Mike it was Luke Redmond who had got her day off to such a bad start that she had spent the rest of the morning desperately trying to get back on schedule. Sensing a vague edginess in Mike, she forced herself to smile. 'I've been looking forward to this.' She looked round the noisy bar and hoped she would be forgiven the lie.

Mike seemed satisfied. He shrugged. 'That's OK.' Any slight hint of peevishness she imagined she heard in his voice vanished with her apology as he proffered the menu. 'I know how it is. I'm just glad you made it, especially under the circumstances. Perhaps we'd better order, or we shan't get any lunch.' He shot her a curious look and Kate frowned, puzzled by his words. What could he possibly mean . . . under the circumstances? What circumstances? She dismissed the thought as Mike looked rather pointedly at his watch and said sheepishly, 'I'm afraid I have to be back in an hour. You know what it's like. Everyone's afraid to step on the new boss's toes.'

Kate laughed. 'I hadn't realised you were so conscientious.'

'Yes, well . . .' Mike grinned. 'New management and all that. There's a lot on. Not that I'm complaining,' he said quickly, almost too quickly, and Kate was puzzled, until she realised that Mike would obviously be bearing the brunt of any changes Luke made.

'I can certainly imagine,' she said drily, guessing what a hardship it must have been to Mike to give up his extended lunch breaks which, she knew from experience, had often run on into mid-afternoon.

Obviously it hadn't taken Luke Redmond long to start making his presence felt. She ordered pâté and toast as a compromise between her lack of appetite and not wanting to offend Mike, and when it came she ate with relish, actually surprised to discover that she was quite hungry. Mike tucked into a pizza and, when they had finished, ordered coffees.

Kate stirred cream and sugar into hers, and sat back with a sigh of satisfaction. 'That was nice. In fact, that's one of the reasons I avoid this place. The food's so good, it can play havoc with a diet.'

'You don't need to diet.' Mike's candid gaze studied the slender curves of her figure in a way Kate found strangely comforting. At least he didn't leave her feeling that she had been mentally stripped naked, as Luke Redmond did. And yet she sensed an odd hint of reserve now, which puzzled her until she thought she guessed the reason.

'Mike, I hope you're not still worrying about what happened.'

He frowned. 'Worrying?'

'Well, blaming yourself, then, because I didn't get the contract with Halliday's. I don't hold you responsible, you do know that?'

For a moment he looked startled, then an uncomfortable flush coloured his cheeks. 'I couldn't exactly blame you if you did, though I swear my hands were tied until everything was signed and sealed. We were all sworn to secrecy, everything was confidential and anyone breaking that confidentiality would have suffered the consequences.' His hand ran through his hair. 'Hell, Kate, I couldn't afford to lose my job, and that's what it would have meant.'

'Yes, I understand. In your position, I expect I'd have done exactly the same thing.' She gave a tight smile, knowing only too well just how ruthless Luke Redmond could be.

Mike still seemed uneasy. 'I suppose I have to admit there was an element of loyalty in it, too.'

'Well, that's perfectly natural.' She bit back a sigh. 'I do understand such things.'

'It's just that . . .' He dropped his gaze to his empty coffee-cup '. . . well, I thought you might feel I owed some to you—loyalty, that is. I mean . . .'

Kate frowned, unable to help him with whatever battle it was he was fighting.

'What is it you're trying to say, Mike?' she snapped, impatient that he wouldn't let the matter drop.

His mouth tightened. 'I suppose I'd rather imagined . . . hoped that we had some sort of relationship.' His eyes rose to look at her directly, and for some reason she sensed that he was angry. 'At least, that was what I thought. It seems I may have made a mistake, in which case I'm sorry. I just wish I'd known, that's all.'

Kate was staring at him, her mouth slightly open on a protest against something she didn't even understand. 'Mike, I don't know what you're talking about. We're friends, *good* friends.'

His mouth twisted wryly. 'Well, I suppose I should be grateful for that at least. I guess I've been pretty naïve in hoping it might be more. I thought you were off men in general, I hadn't figured it was just me. You should have told me how it was between you and

Redmond. I'd have backed off.' He laughed bitterly. 'Believe me, I know I can't win against that sort of competition. I just hadn't reckoned on you falling for his sort. In fact, judging from the way things were the last time the two of you met, I'd say things must have taken a definite turn for the better—he must have used some pretty powerful persuasion.'

By now, Kate was shaking with anger as well as shock. Fumbling clumsily for her bag, she slid out of her seat and marched angrily out of the door, blinking back the tears, hardly caring whether Mike followed or not.

He caught up with her at the door. 'Look, Kate, I'm sorry if I've upset you.'

'Upset me?' Her mouth quivered.

'It was just such a shock, that's all.' He gave her a look of pleading desperation. 'Why in heaven's name didn't you tell me you had someone with you when I phoned? The last thing I wanted was to cause you any embarrassment.'

Her eyes widened in confusion. 'Why on earth should it have done that?'

'I would have thought that was pretty obvious.' Mike dug his hands in his pockets, suddenly looking very sheepish. 'I mean . . . if it had been anyone other than Redmond. You must know the sort of reputation he's got? They say women are lining up to go to bed with him.'

Kate's face was ashen as understanding dawned. 'And you . . . assume that I'm one of "his women", as you so crudely put it? That he . . . I . . .?' Her colour came flooding back.

Mike stared defensively. 'What else am I supposed to think, knowing that he spent the night at your place?'

Kate licked her lips dry, telling herself this was some sort of nightmare. 'And what exactly makes you think that?'

'It seemed pretty obvious,' he said dully. 'I thought when I phoned that you sounded odd. At the time I thought you were upset, now I realise. Hell!'

He broke off abruptly and Kate looked at him, her eyes glittering dangerously, though now she was beginning to suspect that her anger was directed at the wrong person. 'You realise what?' she prompted tautly.

Mike shrugged. 'Well, I guess you were just plain embarrassed. I'm only sorry . . .'

'There's nothing to be sorry about,' Kate snapped. 'I admit Luke Redmond was there when you phoned, but you have no right to assume that he stayed the night. If you don't believe me—ask him.'

He smiled grimly. 'I guess you could say I more or less did that already. Not in so many words,' he added hastily as he saw the stricken look in her eyes. 'I happened to mention after a meeting this morning that I had a lunch date, and he said he knew. He was there at your flat when I made the call. Even then the penny didn't drop, until he said he'd reminded you about it this morning, *before* he left for the office.'

Kate felt sick. He wouldn't . . . he couldn't! But he had, he had deliberately allowed Mike to think that she . . . that they had spent the night together!

'It wasn't like that,' she began to protest thickly.

'Surely you don't believe . . .'

He shrugged. 'Does it matter what I believe?'

Kate had gone very white. 'Yes,' she rasped, 'it matters to me.'

He looked at her for a long moment. 'You mean, he wasn't there last night, and you didn't speak to him this morning?'

'Well . . . yes, he was. I did . . .' Her eyes were wide as she flung a look of appeal at him. 'But it's not what you think.'

Mike's mouth twisted contemptuously. 'So why did he say it, why imply it? Unless he wants people to know he's added you to the list.'

He ignored the hand she flung out towards him. 'I'm sorry I spoiled the little secret, but one thing's for sure, Kate, I won't be waiting around until he drops you. And he will, you can count on it, as soon as he gets tired of you.' He turned away, then back again to smile bitterly. 'The irony is—it's not that I *wouldn't* wait, I *can't*. You see, Mr Redmond has made sure I won't get the chance.'

'Wh-what do you mean?' Kate was fighting hard now to keep the tears in check.

'I heard today, I'm being moved north, out of harm's way.' His smile was derisive. 'I guess he doesn't want any competition, not that there is any, really—is there, Kate? Take care of yourself.'

Without waiting for her reply, he turned and walked away, leaving her to stand on the pavement, seething with shock and outrage. She didn't know why he had chosen to let Mike draw such wrong conclusions, but one thing was for sure, she intended to find out, and he was not going to get away with it.

Her mouth was set in a determined line as she made her way back to her car and the office. The galling thing was that, much as she might protest that she was not Luke's mistress, that they hadn't gone to bed together, her body and the rapid beating of her pulse reminded her all too forcibly of how close she had come to it, and that if he had ignored her protests she would certainly have ended up in bed with him last night! And she wouldn't have regretted it.

CHAPTER FIVE

KATE was sitting in the chair when the doorbell rang. In fact, it rang six times, each time more persistently, before she finally rose to her feet and went to answer it, for the simple reason that she knew that, if she didn't, Luke Redmond was perfectly capable of breaking the door down.

His expression was grim as the dark eyes narrowed, raking her pale face. 'Where the hell were you?' he rasped. 'Didn't you hear me ringing?'

'Yes, I heard you. It would have been difficult not to,' she said resentfully. 'As a matter of fact, I was hoping that if I kept you waiting long enough you'd give up and go away.'

Luke frowned. 'In that case, I'm sorry to disappoint you, Kate, but I don't give up that easily, as you should know by now. Are you going to let me in?' He didn't even wait to be invited, but walked past her into the lounge, leaving her no choice but to follow, battling with her resentment and some other feeling which she absolutely refused to recognise as panic.

She faced him across the room, her green eyes blazing angrily. 'Are you always so damned arrogant? This is my home! You have no God-given right to walk in as if you own it and . . .'

'And *you*, Kate?' The words were drawled softly as

he stood looking at her. 'Is that what you were going to say?'

She blushed furiously. 'No, it wasn't.' He was doing it again, she thought, as the dark gaze wandered lazily over her face, making her feel vulnerable, trapped. She stood her ground, but her legs felt ridiculously weak as his eyes narrowed dangerously.

'So, are you going to tell me why you weren't going to answer the door? And better still,' the dark gaze flickered over the skirt and blouse she was wearing, 'why you're not ready? I was under the impression we had a date.'

'I changed my mind.'

'Just like that?' His eyes narrowed to dark slits. 'You mean you've decided to chicken out.'

'No!' She licked her lips nervously as he came towards her threateningly, only to stop as she gave a slight moan. A flicker of concern briefly flashed over the handsome features. His glance had already taken in the half-drawn curtains and the chair with its crumpled cushion where she had obviously been sitting.

'You're not ill, are you, Kate?' he rasped anxiously.

'No.'

'Then . . . perhaps you'd better explain.'

'I believe it's a woman's privilege. Not that I suppose you know anything about that do you, Mr Redmond? I don't suppose you're accustomed to having your women turn you down.' She knew from the sudden grim tightening of his mouth that she had said the wrong thing, but she refused to let Luke Redmond intimidate her, especially here on her own ground, where she should feel safe. But that was precisely what he was doing, whether intentionally or otherwise. Every feature of the tanned face, every muscle in the taut, proud frame offered a threat, and her hand flew to her throat to stifle a feeling of panic.

'I have to admit,' he conceded softly, 'it's not happened so far.'

'Well, now it has. I'm afraid I have no intention of pandering to your ego.'

'I don't quite see what my ego has to do with any of this.'

'Don't you?' she flung at him hotly. 'Don't you really? Well, in that case, perhaps you can explain to me why you told Mike that you . . . I . . .' She licked her lips. 'That we . . .'

'That we what, Kate?'

She swallowed hard, unable to bring herself to look at him. 'That we . . .'

'Spent the night together?' Luke said it for her, quietly. 'Is that what you're trying to say, Kate?'

She eyed him coldly. 'You know very well it is.' She turned away, waves of humiliation washing over her.

Firm hands grasped her arms, turning her to face him. 'And what really annoys you, Kate? The fact that it's not true—or the fact that your boyfriend thinks it is?'

She flushed at the softly spoken words, aware of the disturbingly sensual mouth. 'You're despicable!'

He gave a husky laugh. 'I'm not responsible for what your boyfriend thinks, Kate. Not that I blame him for being jealous.'

Anger flashed in her green eyes. 'Mike is *not* my

boyfriend, not in the sense you're implying. We're just good friends . . .'

'As the actress said . . .'

'Why you . . .' Her hand rose, only to be caught in a vice-like grip, and suddenly the laughter had gone from his eyes.

'Don't do it, Kate,' he warned softly. 'I might have to retaliate, and I don't think you're quite ready yet for what I have in mind.' He looked at her and she blushed furiously. 'Not that I'm not willing to find out. Just take it as a warning, Kate. As yet, you've no idea just what I'm capable of.'

'I have no desire to find out.' she told him forcibly, and saw his mouth twist.

'We'll see about that.' He looked at his watch and raised dark eyebrows. 'Right now, it's getting late and we have a table booked. You'd better go and change.'

She blinked. 'You don't seriously still expect me to go out with you?'

He frowned. 'I fail to see why not. We had an arrangement—as far as I'm concerned nothing has changed. In fact, not only do I *expect*,' he cut in fiercely, 'I *insist*.'

'But I haven't changed.'

He gave her a long, steady look. 'I can wait, but if you try any delaying tactics, I shall be obliged to come and offer my assistance,' he taunted softly.

She gasped, 'You wouldn't dare!'

His eyebrows rose. 'Unless, of course, you'd prefer to stay here, in which case I'm sure we could find some interesting way to spend the evening!'

She recognised that she was fighting a losing battle

and hated him for it. At the same time, the last thing she wanted was an evening alone with him.

Anger blazed in her eyes. 'You win. I'll go and get changed, but on condition that you remember this is strictly business.'

Cool dark eyes regarded her expressionlessly. 'I always keep my word. Besides—I'm sure you'll agree, there's safety in numbers.'

Kate threw him a scathing look before heading for the bedroom where, after a moment's hesitation, she locked the door. The trouble with Luke Redmond was that she didn't know if anything guaranteed safety where he was concerned.

Sitting in front of the mirror, she brushed her hair until it fell in soft waves against her face. She applied a light covering of make-up, her green eyes, framed by extravagantly dark lashes, needing little emphasis.

It would have been easier, of course, if she had had the presence of mind to ask where they were going, but she refused to give him the satisfaction of doing so now. She would just have to settle for something suitably in between—not too dressy, not too formal.

In the event, she chose a dress for its sheer simplicity, a dress of navy chiffon with full skirts and a starkly white collar, long sleeves and pearl-buttoned cuffs. The fact that the bodice moulded to her figure, that the skirts emphasised the tiny waist and slender hips, was something of which she was completely unaware as she stared at her reflection in the long mirror and gave a nod of satisfaction. The effect was completed by a pair of high-heeled strappy sandals.

Prim was the word she would have used to describe

it—until she saw the swift look of approval in Luke's eyes as he rose to his feet when she finally walked into the room.

His gaze narrowed and lingered for a long moment, halting her involuntarily in her tracks.

'I was just about to come and fetch you,' he said. 'I'm almost glad I didn't.'

She eyed him uncertainly. 'Do I take it you approve?'

'Wasn't I supposed to?' he laughed huskily.

'I really didn't take your opinion into account,' protested Kate, walking ahead of him through the door, but there was something decidedly confusing about the slight tremor of excitement which ran through her as he placed a proprietorial hand on her arm to help her into the car.

'Where exactly are we going?' she asked as he settled himself in the seat beside her.

He was concentrating on edging out into the traffic. 'Somewhere where the food is good, the waiters don't hover and they don't believe in loud music.' He turned his head to look at her. 'It's also Greek owned and run. You don't dislike Greek food?'

'I've never actually tried it before.'

His mouth twisted. 'In that case, it will be yet another new experience. I'm sure you'll enjoy it.'

Kate deliberately turned to stare out of the window, trying to shake off a feeling of resentment. Luke Redmond was far too sure of what would please her. However, she couldn't resist a tiny gasp of pleasure as the car drew up outside the restaurant.

Their arrival was greeted by the head waiter who,

from the way he rushed towards them hands out-
stretched, obviously recognised Luke.

'My old friend! Is good to see you again. Where
have you been for so long? We've missed you.'

'You know how it is, Leo. Business.'

'Ah!' The Greek raised his hands in the air. 'A man
must still eat.'

Luke laughed and Kate watched, intrigued, as the
two men exchanged greetings before they were led to
a secluded table set in an alcove. The curtains had
been drawn across the windows, there were fresh
flowers on the table and a candle flickered. It all
bespoke an intimacy which brought a sudden and
unexpected tightness to her throat, so that she
hesitated momentarily.

'Is something wrong?' The faint note of concern in
his voice drew her up with a start.

'No.' She sat quickly in the chair Leo was holding
for her. 'This is fine.' She eyed Luke sceptically. 'It's
not exactly what I'd expected for a business
discussion, that's all.'

His mouth quirked. 'There's no reason we can't be
civilised about it. It so happens that I enjoy eating
here. We could easily have gone somewhere more
private. Would you have preferred that?'

Kate's mouth tightened at the hint of mockery in
his voice. 'It really doesn't matter. As you said, the
least we can do is try to be civilised.' She smiled at
Leo, who had returned with the menus, and focused
her attention deliberately on the pages. Her
expression changed rapidly to one of confusion.
Finally, to Luke's obvious amusement, she had to

admit defeat. 'I'm sorry, I know everything is translated into English, but I have no idea what to choose.'

'Then I'm afraid it looks as if for once you'll have to trust me, or is that asking too much?'

She threw him a quelling look. 'On the subject of food, I'm prepared to accept your judgement. After all, you're the expert, and I'm not difficult to please.'

His eyes darkened to fathomless pools of jet. 'Oh, but I'd say you were very discerning, Kate. A little cautious perhaps, but when you find the courage I'm sure the results will be far more rewarding than you could ever have imagined.'

Her cheeks blushed fiercely red as she realised he had deliberately given a double edge to the words. 'I was talking about the food.'

'Yes, of course. What else?'

She bit back a protest as he gave their order to Leo, then listened, fascinated, as the two men lapsed into what she knew must be Greek. For the first time, as she watched them laughing together, it struck her that he was completely at ease here, that these were his people. It was only as both men turned to look at her that she guessed she had become the subject of their conversation, and she smiled nervously, waiting until Leo had taken their order and left before saying defensively, 'What did he say?'

Luke shrugged. 'I asked about his family. Leo has a great many sisters and brothers, cousins and aunts . . . In return, I felt obliged to satisfy his curiosity about us.'

'I wouldn't have thought there was anything to

satisfy.'

'Don't be offended,' he said quickly. 'The Greeks like to ask questions, and when they know all about you, you become a friend for life.'

She swallowed hard. 'What did you tell him?'

His eyebrows rose. 'What could I tell him, Kate? Leo sees any beautiful girl in terms of a wife and many babies—I said the English were more reserved. Something Leo puts down to your miserable climate.'

'*Our* climate?' Kate put the question and realised she suddenly felt shy as he looked at her through the halo of light from the candle. 'I always wondered . . . I mean . . . I'm just curious to know how you come to be part of a Greek company.'

He shrugged. 'Let's just say I have family connections with Greece.'

'But you are . . .' She looked at the dark hair and tanned features.

'British?' He laughed softly. 'As British as you are, Kate. My mother was Greek. My father was serving with the British Army when they met. She was just nineteen and he was twenty-three.' He looked at her in silence for a long moment. 'My mother was working for the Greek resistance. That was how she met my father. He was with a small group, carrying out some reconnaissance work.' His mouth twisted. 'Basically, spying on the enemy. Once their cover was blown, they had to go into hiding. Two of them were captured. One was shot, and two others, one of them my father, were found by the Greek resistance and taken to a safe place up in the mountains.' He laughed. 'At least, it was as safe as any place could be. In fact, they had to be moved around, constantly keeping ahead of the German troops. The people from the villages took enormous risks supplying them with food. Had they been caught, they knew they all faced the possibility of death—men, women and children alike.'

'And it was your mother who led them?' Kate breathed raggedly.

He nodded, his expression bitter. 'My father was badly wounded when they almost walked straight into a German advance guard. He was shot.'

'Oh, no!' Her hand tightened over his.

'They managed to get him away, but it was a bad leg wound. My mother nursed him as well as she could, and he pulled through, more or less.' He smiled bleakly. 'I suppose it was almost inevitable that they should fall in love.'

Kate swallowed hard, trying to imagine the courage it had needed to do what that simple Greek girl had done. Her eyes brimmed with tears. In spite of her feelings for this man, she could begin to understand something now of the forces which drove him, the feelings and inherited passions which were an inherent part of him.

'What happened?' she asked.

Luke's mouth tightened. 'They married after the war. My father brought my mother to England to meet his family. I was born here.'

Her lips twitched involuntarily. 'Somehow I find it difficult to imagine you as small and helpless.'

He returned her smile with an unexpectedness which caught her completely off guard. 'I assure you,

Kate, I was in every way a perfectly normal, healthy child.'

She felt the embarrassed colour creep into her cheeks, and withdrew her hand quickly from his as the cool, dark eyes deliberately seemed to taunt her. 'I'll take your word for it. Did your parents stay in England?'

It was as if a shutter came down over the dark eyes, and she was shocked by the sudden tensing of his hands. 'No. My father's wound had never healed properly. He began to feel the effects more and more. I suspect, too, that after the years spent in Greece he had fallen in love with the place as well as with my mother, in spite of the war. They decided to go home. My father died a year later.'

Kate felt her heart give a painful jolt. 'So you were raised by your mother?'

'She was killed in a car accident when I was eight years old.' The hand Kate reached out to him was held for a few brief seconds. 'It was a long time ago, Kate. I didn't even know my father, and the memories I have of my mother are all good. I was brought up a grandfather I idolised, and there were dozens of aunts, uncles and cousins to see to it that I didn't suffer for the loss. So one thing I don't need is pity.'

'I wasn't aware that I was offering any,' she said hotly.

He leaned forward, frowning. 'Then what is it, Kate?'

She gave him a quick, nervous glance, and was saved the necessity of a reply by the arrival of their food. It served as an excuse to relieve the tension which had suddenly somehow sparked between them.

'This looks good. What is it?'

'Taramosalata. Fish roe. I think you'll like it. It has a very delicate flavour.' He studied the wine list. 'Do you have any particular preference for red or white wine?'

She fumbled with her knife. 'I don't drink.'

'Everyone drinks, Kate.'

'I mean . . . alcohol.'

'Is that on religious or moral grounds?' He ordered retsina and fruit juice before lifting his gaze to study her troubled face.

'It's on the grounds that I prefer non-alcoholic drinks,' she said firmly.

'Well, I hope you approve of the food, at least. I've ordered *souvlaki* to follow.'

'*Souvlaki?*'

'Pork kebabs, except that in Greece we don't refer to them as kebabs.'

Kate was surprised to find that she had suddenly developed an appetite, and she enjoyed the experience of eating different foods.

'You were right,' she conceded. 'That was lovely. I doubt if I would have opted for fish roe if you'd told me in advance that that's what it was.'

Luke sat back, waiting for the second course to be served. 'You should have more spirit of adventure.'

Two spots of colour swam into her cheeks. 'Let's just say I'm naturally cautious about most new things. I find it's far safer.'

'Nothing is safe, Kate. Sooner or later you'll have to come out and face the world. The only alternative is to spend your life behind locked doors. But perhaps if you're scared enough you'll end up doing just that.'

Her eyes were stormy as she looked at him across the table. 'Why should it matter to you what I do with my life?'

'Because I hate waste, and I do have an interest.'

Her breathing was ragged as she picked up her fork to toy with her food. 'As far as I'm concerned, the only interest we could ever possibly have in common, Mr Redmond, is strictly business, and I prefer to keep it that way. Or did you being me here under false pretences? If so, I can easily leave.' She had already half risen from her chair when his hand closed over her wrist.

'Damn you, sit down and eat your food!' Anger blazed from his dark eyes. 'I won't have my friends think their hospitality isn't to your liking.'

For a moment, she stared down at him with equal fury. 'You're sure it's not your own reputation you're worried about? It must be quite a new experience, Luke Redmond actually being walked out on.'

He was on his feet too now, breathing angrily. 'Don't play games with me, Kate. It's far too dangerous a pastime.'

She pulled away from his restraining hand on her arm, colour darkening her cheeks. 'I wasn't aware that *I* was playing games. You gave your word.'

He drew a harsh breath. 'And I'll keep it, damn you, but be warned, Kate, there are limits to the amount of restraint I possess. *I want you.*'

She swallowed convulsively, tautly aware of the sheer physical magnetism of this man, the heady

perfume of musk aftershave, the cool, frightening
determination.

She sat down shakily.

'Thank you,' he said softly.

Leo hovered, his expression troubled. 'Everything
is all right? The food . . .'

'Is superb, thank you, Leo.' Kate couldn't bring
herself to look at Luke. 'I . . . I thought I'd left my
handbag in the car and panicked, but it's here.' She
showed him the slim bag, and Leo went away happy.

'Thank you for that,' Luke said. 'Leo is one of my
dearest friends.'

She made yet another attempt to eat, pushing the
food round her plate. 'I'm sorry.'

'No,' his mouth tightened grimly, '*I'm* sorry.
Where you're concerned, *agapi mou*, it seems I have a
lot to learn about self-control and God knows I'm not
finding it easy.' He seemed to share her own lack of
appetite, and reached for his wine instead. 'Let's talk
business,' he said hoarsely.

Kate looked across the table, confused by the
sudden withdrawal. 'Luke . . .'

'I take it you have read the report I left with you?'

'Yes.' A faint flush coloured her cheeks. 'As a
matter of fact, I did.'

'In spite of not being interested?' His smile was
deiberately provocative again, yet somehow she felt
more at ease with that than his anger.

'I didn't say I wasn't interested in the project, only
that I didn't want to work for you.'

'I had in mind that you would work *with* me, rather
than for me.' He picked up his fork again. 'Give me

your thoughts on the report.'

She frowned. 'It's an ambitious project.'

'Poseidon is a big company with an equally big reputation. What we're looking for here is no different to what we already have in the rest of the world. First-class hotel accommodation, leisure and conference facilities.'

'So, I have to ask,' Kate looked at him steadily, 'why me? There must be dozens, hundreds of well-established designers who could produce what you're looking for.'

'You're right, there are, and each would bring along his or her own well-established ideas.' He sat back. 'What I'm looking for is someone with a totally new outlook, someone uninhibited by years of mass design. I've looked at the work you produced for Halliday's. It was quite naïvely brilliant.'

Kate gave a harsh laugh. 'That sounds remarkably like an insult.'

'Because I call it naïve?' he mocked. 'You misunderstand me. Perhaps I should have said it had an uncluttered freshness, none of the stereotyping I'm trying so hard to avoid. What I want is someone with a feel for the Poseidon image.'

'I'm not at all sure I know what that is. A report gives only facts.'

'We are Greek.'

The simple statement was, for him, enough, she realised, feeling her heartbeat quicken as their eyes met across the table. She tried to look away but couldn't. The jet-dark eyes held hers and refused to let go, making her, for the first time, aware of that side of him which was timeless, inherited from his ancestors, the gods of legend.

'I wish I'd been to Greece.'

'You would fall in love with it, and the Greeks would love you.' His hand lightly caressed her cheek, touched a strand of her hair. 'You would be stared at. The Greeks like beauty.' His mouth tightened and he sat back again. 'You must go there some day.'

Not, 'I will take you there', simply that she must go. Why did she feel a pang of disappointment?

'Perhaps I will, one day. I still don't happen to think any of this makes me a likely candidate for the job you have in mind.'

'It scares you?' asked Luke quietly.

'No.' Her head went up. 'I've already told you it doesn't scare me.'

'Then what is holding you back, Kate? Or need I ask?'

'Probably not.' Her tone was sharp as she looked at him. 'The simple truth is that I don't think I care to work for you.'

He gave an angry sigh. 'You realise what you'd be turning down?'

'Apart from the unwelcome attentions of my boss, you mean?' She couldn't resist the taunt, and saw him whiten. 'Oh, yes, I've calculated the cost.'

'And you can dismiss it so easily?'

She stared into the depths of her glass. 'Not easily, no.'

'Then you're less of a businesswoman that I took you for if you can think of refusing for reasons which are strictly personal.'

Kate's eyes widened. 'How can you say that when you've made no secret of the fact that . . . that . . .'

'That I want you, Kate? I don't deny it.'

Her eyes darkened. 'I find your kind of ruthlessness hard to live with. You don't give a damn about the people whose lives you tear apart, about those people at Halliday's. About Mike.' Her sarcasm was barely contained. 'I'd be interested to hear your motives for moving him.'

'I take it you've already discussed it,' he said drily.

'Obviously. We had lunch together, remember?'

'In that case, I don't doubt he was at pains to give you his own opinion on the subject.'

'As a matter of fact, he did. He thinks . . . that is, he has the idea that it's personal, that you want him out of the way.' She licked dry lips.

'I see.' The dark eyes glittered in mocking challenge. 'And did he explain to you just why he thinks I should go to the trouble of . . . getting him out of the way?'

Kate blushed furiously. 'You know damn well why. You deliberately allowed him to believe that we . . . that we are lovers. He thinks this is your way of removing the competition.'

His eyes narrowed. 'I'd say your friend has a high opinion of himself. But what do you think, Kate?'

Her hand shook as she set her glass down. 'I think I'm only just beginning to realise precisely what you're capable of, that you're the kind of man who doesn't let anything or anyone get in his way. I think you're capable of anything.'

He didn't look at her. 'And you care for him, is that

it?'

She frowned. 'He's a friend, a good friend, and that happens to mean something to me.' She bit her lip. 'Can't you reconsider sending him up north?'

His mouth twisted with cruel cynicism. 'You're actually pleading for him?'

'No.' She drew in an angry breath. 'I'm *asking* you to think again. After all,' her voice softened. 'if you don't seriously see Mike as competition, what have you to lose?'

'I think only you would know the answer to that, Kate.' His eyes raked over her face with chilling intensity. 'I'm not in the habit of reconsidering my decisions. However, since it means so much to you, perhaps we can made a deal.'

She caught the look of triumph which glittered briefly in the dark eyes before it was quickly masked. Her breath caught in her throat.

'Wh-what sort of deal exactly?'

He leaned forwards, his finger caressing the curve of her flushed cheek. 'Shall we say your . . . services, in return for your boyfriend's job, wherever it may be?'

CHAPTER SIX

BRILLIANT colour flamed into Kate's cheeks as she stared at him. 'My services?'

Luke looked at her with cool deliberation. 'Is it too much to ask? If so, I'm sure Forrest will understand when you explain. After all, he's probably a reasonable fellow at heart.'

She stared at him, her eyes wide with shock. 'You bastard!'

His mouth twisted. 'Does the idea really offend you so much? I wonder why? It seems to me that your boyfriend's job should be worth your name on a contract. But, of course, if you don't think so . . .'

'Contract?' She threw him a startled look, blushing before the cool mockery in his eyes.

'I've never yet had to resort to blackmail in order to get a woman into my bed, Kate, if that's what you were thinking.'

She threw him a scathing glance. 'You mean they were all eager and willing, of course.'

'Let's just say I've had no complaints so far.'

She bit back a sharp retort. 'I already have a contract.'

'Drawn up with Halliday's. I prefer my own.'

She eyed him warily. 'Do I have any choice?'

'Not a great deal,' drawled Luke softly. 'On the

100

other hand, it will all be perfectly legal, Kate, and the gains won't be purely and simply on my side.'

She looked down at her plate. 'And that's all you want, my signature on a contract?'

'It's what I'll settle for, Kate—for now. I'd want a written draft report setting out your ideas, costings and so on, on my desk within the week, and I shall need to discuss the ideas with you before I put them to my board.'

'It *sounds* reasonable.'

'If you're looking for catches, I assure you there are none. Do we shake hands on a deal, or seal it with a kiss?'

Kate bit back a scathing retort as the waiter returned to remove their plates, and Leo flourished the menu. It had been in her mind to refuse a sweet, but now a spark of mischief took over.

'Why don't you let me choose the next course?' She smiled disarmingly at him.

'Why not?' He raised one dark eyebrow, but she was giving her full attention to the menu.

'Now, this sounds very nice.'

Leo followed her pointing finger, nodding his approval. 'Ah, yes. Is *kataïfi.* Kat-eye-fee,' he enunciated for her benefit, 'is honey and nuts in filo pastry.' He made a little *moue* of doubt. 'Is *very* sweet.'

Kate snapped the menu to a close. 'In that case, it will do very nicely for Mr Redmond. His temper needs all the sweetening it can get. I'll just have coffee—*without* sugar. Thank you, Leo.'

She heard Luke make a soft choking sound in his

throat as Leo ambled away, laughing softly to himself.

'Satisfied?' Luke growled.

'Not anywhere near,' she glared at him. 'But it will do for now.'

Behind the candleglow, she sensed that he smiled. 'I take it this means you have no objection to signing the new contract?'

'Are you prepared to take the risk that I might let you down?'

'I don't think that's very likely, not even out of a desire for revenge. I think you're astute enough to enjoy the challenge of the Poseidon. I have faith in you, Kate.' His eyes darkened. 'I know you'll give me what I want, sooner or later, and I'm prepared to wait.'

Kate looked at him and felt a sensation of pure excitement run through her. She could deny it aloud as much as she liked, but the sheer sensuality, the animal magnetism of him sent a wave of desire rushing like a flame through her body.

'Luke, I . . .'

He frowned, then, very slowly, his expression changed to one of something like wonderment. 'Kate?'

'No, please don't.' She tried to evade the hand which imprisoned her own. 'I'm too confused.'

He drew a ragged breath. 'I'd never hurt you, you know that. Trust me.'

She swallowed hard. 'I do.' The trouble was, it was already too late, she was already hurting in a way she had promised herself she would never be hurt again.

She barely tasted the strong, sweet Greek coffee Leo placed before her. Luke left untouched the sweet she had ordered. He said something in Greek to Leo as he paid the bill, then his hand was under her arm as he escorted her out to the car.

'It was a lovely meal,' she said after he had closed the door behind her and gone round to the driver's seat.

'What you ate of it.' He didn't look at her as he eased the Porsche into the traffic, and Kate was glad. She opened a window to let the breeze cool her cheeks, but it did nothing to lessen the tension which seemed to crackle between them like static electricity.

It was a relief when they drew up outside the flat, but if she had hoped to be able to make her escape she felt a surge of panic as he got out to stand beside her.

'There's no need for you to come to the door,' she said weakly. 'I'm rather tired, so if you don't mind I'd rather say goodnight here.' She held out her hand, to be treated to a look of gentle scorn.

'I'm not in the habit of leaving a woman standing on the doorstep, Kate.' He took the keys from her nerveless grasp and unlocked the door. But he made no attempt to leave. 'Isn't it the custom to ask a date in for one last drink?'

'It . . . it isn't *my* custom,' she said tautly, willing him not to pursue it. She wasn't prepared for him to kiss her. For a split second she resisted, fighting the steel-hard tension of his body as he drew her against him, his mouth urgently seeking hers.

'Don't run away from me, Kare,' he ground out before his lips claimed hers, assaulting their softness, making her gasp as a shock-wave of desire ran through her. Involuntarily, she gave a low moan of pleasure, arching her body towards him, shuddering slightly as his hands caressed the curving sweep of her lips, moulding her against him.

It was several seconds before she realised that he was gradually, imperceptibly, robbing her of the little control she still had. Wrenching her mouth free, she pushed him away, breathing hard. 'This is crazy!'

'You're right,' he said thickly. 'I don't think the neighbours would appreciate my making love to you on the doorstep, but that's what's likely to happen if you don't invite me in.' He was breathing deeply, and she knew that he was fighting hard to regain self-control. 'You must know the effect you have on me, Kate?'

She blushed, unable to deny that she had been only too aware of his state of arousal. Her own heart was beating so loudly that she was certain he must hear it, too. She was shocked by what was happening. For too long she had lived with a kind of sexual numbness, believing herself immune to the sort of emotions and desires he was forcing her to face now. It was a theory she had never even been tempted to test, simply because without feeling there was no pain, and that was the way she preferred it. Or so she had managed to fool herself, until now.

Pale with the shock of realisation, she faced him, glad of some last deeply ingrained instinct of self-preservation which enabled her to speak calmly.

'I can offer you coffee.' Her fingers shook as she fumbled with the key he had dropped into her out-stretched hand and opened the door. 'I only keep cheap brandy for medicinal purposes.'

'I don't need brandy, Kate,' he said quietly. 'When we make love, I intend for us both to be stone-cold sober.' He came slowly towards her, and with soft, angry curse took possession of her mouth in a brutal, unrelenting kiss.

Desperately Kate tried to resist, forcing her body to remain rigid, knowing that if she weakened she was lost. His hands roamed convulsively over her body, fumbling with the buttons of her dress until he reached the soft, warm texture of her skin, and she heard the soft rasp of satisfaction in his throat as she arched involuntarily towards him.

She closed her eyes as his mouth teased then claimed hers, and she moaned as the pent-up agony of desire broke through the barriers of her self-restraint. With a sob, her arms reached up, drawing him closer.

Luke made an inarticulate sound deep in his throat and, with barely a second's hesitation, he swept her up in his arms and carried her through to the bedroom. In a single movement he went down with her on to the bed, pinning her beneath him as he freed her of the restriction of her clothes, before his mouth began yet another tormenting exploration of her burning skin.

In a brief moment of panic, Kate resisted as he imprisoned her own feverishly searching hands, one muscular thigh parting her legs. 'I want you, Kate,' he said thickly. 'You know this was bound to happen.'

With deft movements he had removed his own clothing, and she became aware of the heat of their bodies as his head came down to her shoulder. In a purely instinctive reaction, her teeth teased hungrily against his skin as her fingers began tracing the silk-smooth curve of his back. She felt him move spasmodically.

'Give yourself to me, Kate . . .'

She turned her face up to his and shivered beneath the steel-dark glitter of his eyes, and then, as if to exorcise a ghost, she reached up and put her arms round his neck, her fingers twining in the dark hair.

Waves of pleasure coursed through her as Luke lifted her, drew her closer still, until she could feel the thud of his heartbeat. He looked down at her. 'You know I have to make love to you.'

She closed her eyes, wanting it to happen, but suddenly her own heart was racing out of control at what he was doing to her. It was all happening too fast. She hadn't meant it to happen at all!

She twisted her head from side to side, until he caught her face in his hands, silencing her whimpers of protest with his mouth. There was no escape. The more she fought, the more helpless she became, as he seemed to use even her struggles against her. As her body arched, torn between resistance and the sensuality of his kiss, his weight shifted, and she found to her cost that she had made it easier for him. What he was doing was an invasion of every instinct, everything she had clung to. That most private, precious part, which she had only shared with Steve in the first heady, most beautiful days of their marriage.

She gasped, her eyes widening as his hand traced her naked skin, over her hips, the flatness of her stomach, lower and lower still, until she groaned, closing her eyes tight against the arrogant certainty she saw in his eyes.

'No!' The cry was wrung from her even as she trembled in a daze of pleasure.

'Yes, Kate, yes,' he ground out, forcing her legs apart to receive the rough hardness of his fully aroused body. 'Let me love you. Love *me*, Kate, love me.'

Her skin was on fire, tortured by a driving need to have him possess her completely. It was a purely primeval feeling, like nothing she ever experienced before, even with Steve.

She moved beneath him, catching her breath as he drew her ruthlessly into the taut hardness of his thighs. Her head went back as he tormented her, rousing her still further, patiently controlling his own need until she could bear it no longer.

She willed herself not to react, not to give him the satisfaction he sought, and was forcing her to give.

His hands caressed her cheek, moved to the silk-softness of her breasts, gentling, trying to still her panic. 'I won't hurt you, Kate,' he said huskily. 'Just don't fight me. Trust me.'

She *did* trust him. She knew beyond all reason that she wanted him, desired him with every throbbing fibre of her being, but she also knew that with that final surrender the pain would begin all over again.

She gave a small, inarticulate cry, and suddenly she was pushing against him. The salt taste of tears was in her mouth as she looked up and saw the look of disbelief and then of raw pain in his eyes as he stared down at her.

'Kate, what is it? What's wrong?'

Her hands pushed against his chest. 'I can't . . . I just can't.'

She felt a tremor run through her as his hands tightened on her wrists. 'Don't do this to me, Kate,' he rasped. 'I want you. You want me.'

'No.' She closed her eyes tight in an attempt to shut out the bitter incredulity she saw in his taut features, before his hands moved beneath her back.

'Yes.' His body covered hers. 'Do I have to prove it to you? Because I can.' But as his hand began its pleasurable teasing she flinched, and he recoiled instantly, as if she had struck him.

Bewilderment seared across his face as he tensed above her. 'Don't tell me you don't want me because I don't believe it,' he said raggedly. 'Have I hurt you so much that you're afraid?'

'No.' She looked at him through a blur of tears. 'It isn't that.'

'Then what? In God's name, tell me!'

She turned her head away, but he still held her trapped beneath the greater strength of his body. She knew she could never win, not in a display of physical superiority. Her only ally against him had to be words.

'Because I won't go through that kind of agony again. I loved my husband, and neither you nor anyone else can take that from me.'

For a moment, she was actually afraid of the dark anger she saw in his eyes as he looked down at her. 'You're lying, Kate. Perhaps you don't know it, but your body couldn't respond to me as it does . . . like this.'

Her breathing quickened convulsively. 'Is it so inconceivable to you that I might be telling the truth, that I don't want you to make love to me?'

His eyes glittered. 'What is inconceivable to me is that you can fool yourself. He's dead, Kate!'

A sob caught in her throat. 'That doesn't mean I've forgotten.'

'I'm not asking you to forget,' ground out Luke savagely. 'I'm telling you that love isn't that selfish. You can't sacrifice the rest of your life to the memory of a dead man.' Brutally, he forced her to look at him. 'What did he do to you, Kate? What hold has he got over you that you can't . . . daren't let go and admit that you have feelings?'

'He died, damn you! Isn't that enough?'

'You're hiding from reality, Kate,' he insisted passionately. 'He's dead, and I'm very much alive. God knows, I want you.'

She tried to fight the rising tide of passion that was engulfing her as he moved towards her and, with slow deliberation, took her in his arms. It had been so long since she had felt such need. Too long since her body had felt anything at all. Was he right, that Steve wouldn't expect her to live her life with nothing but memories? Was that what she wanted?

A nerve pulsed in her throat, and she stiffened in his arms. She felt his hands tighten.

'Kate . . .'

'No . . . no, please don't.' She couldn't go through it all again—all the loving and then the pain.

'Kate, what *is* it?' She saw the anguish in his eyes as

she fought him, panicked by the realisation that she had come so close to surrender.

'I can't.' She wrenched herself away from him. 'I won't be hurt again. I've been through it and I don't intend to let it happen again, not a second time.'

He was moving away from her, pushing aside the single sheet which had covered them. She watched, trembling as he began to pull on his clothes before turning to look at her.

'You can't run away for ever, Kate.' His voice was grim. 'Sooner or later, you'll have to come out of hiding and start fighting. Well, I can wait. I don't give up this easily. Some day you'll beg me to make love to you.'

Humiliation washed over her like an ice-cold wave as he looked down at her. Right now she was all too painfully aware of her own vulnerability where Luke Redmond was concerned, but she had her life too neatly mapped out to let emotions intrude, disturbing her safety. All the same, she shivered as the words hung in the air like a threat, long after he had closed the door behind him.

CHAPTER SEVEN

KATE buzzed the intercom on her desk. 'Jenny, I'm still waiting for that call to Poseidon International. What's the hold-up? I'm due to go out in about half an hour.'

'I'm sorry, Kate. I'm still trying, but Mr Redmond's secretary insists he's still unavailable.'

'I see.' Kate's mouth tightened. 'OK, thanks, Jenny.'

There was a fractional pause. 'Do you want me to keep trying?'

'No, that's all right, Jenny, forget it.' Kate leaned forwards again. 'Look, why don't you go for lunch now? And take that extra half-hour you wanted to do some shopping.'

'I really don't mind staying on and trying the number again.'

Kate smiled. 'No, that's nice of you, Jen, but I think it would be a waste of time. It's a bit late now, anyway. The meeting is scheduled for an hour's time. You go. I'll sort something out.' She sat back, fingers drumming angrily against the desk. 'I don't believe it, he's doing this on purpose,' she muttered, turning to Sue.

'Perhaps he is genuinely busy.' Sue earned herself a derisive look.

'For two whole days?'

'Well, I suppose it is possible.'

'Oh, come on!' Kate snapped.

Sue shrugged. 'So what are you going to do?'

Kate glanced impatiently from the check list she had been working on to her gold watch. 'Do? That's simple. I intend keeping my original appointment with Lorna.'

'He's going to be furious, you do realise that? When you fail to turn up at that meeting with the preliminary draft of ideas and figures, he's going to make trouble with a capital T.'

Kate rose forcibly to her feet and dropped a file into the cabinet. 'I fail to see how I can be held responsible when I wasn't even consulted about the arrangement. And anyway, whose side are you on?'

'Hey, it isn't a question of taking sides.'

Kate took a deep breath and held it in an effort to control a surge of anger. 'If he'd had the decency to consult me first as to whether or not I could make it, instead of just assuming . . .' She swept a hand forcibly through her hair. 'I can't break my lunch date with Lorna. I made the arrangement over a week ago, and she leaves for Birmingham tomorrow.'

'I take it you've tried leaving a message with his secretary?'

'Yes, of course, but all I get is the same response. "I'm extremely sorry," Kate mimicked, "Mr Redmond is still unavailable but the moment he gets in touch or returns to his office . . ."'

'Well,' Sue shook her head, 'I hate to say it, but that contract you signed does give him certain rights.'

'But not the right to make specific demands on my time without at least some prior consultation, and a formal little memo in the post two days before a meeting isn't prior consultation in my book.'

Sue gave her a sideways glance. 'Look, would it help if I were to deliver the draft report?'

'You'd be prepared to do that?'

Sue shrugged. 'Can you come up with a better solution?'

'Offhand, no,' Kate said thickly. 'I can't say I can.'

'Well, in that case, it's settled.'

'Look, you don't have to do this.'

'You're right, I don't. On the other hand, we *are* partners. We've gone over the specifications together, we've discussed the figures.'

'He's still bound to come up with questions.'

'So, I'll answer them to the best of my ability. Is that the report?'

'Here.' Kate handed over the file and Sue grinned.

'But I don't see any blue touch-paper.'

In spite of the seriousness of the situation, Kate laughed. 'We could always send it by special messenger.'

'Somehow I suspect that when Luke Redmond says "in person", he means just that. By the way,' she paused at the door, 'what do you want me to do if he needs to set up another meeting?'

'We have a perfectly competent secretary.' Kate's tone was aggressive. 'Tell him to call Jenny. She'll let him know when I'm free.'

Sue chuckled. 'I think I'll go before I change my mind. Give my regards to Lorna, and tell her I hope the new job works out.'

'Well, if it doesn't, we know who to thank, don't we?' Kate said crossly.

'I'll see you later.'

Kate waved and reached for the phone. Five minutes later, shrugging herself into a cream linen jacket, she stepped into a taxi and sat back, doing her best to dispell an uneasy feeling that she had merely postponed rather than escaped a further confrontation with Luke Redmond. For the moment, however, with memories of their last meeting still all too fresh in her mind, even this brief respite was something she felt grateful for.

She gave herself a mental shake as the taxi drew to a halt, paid the driver and was actually smiling as she walked into the restaurant.

Kate sat back, having given her order to the waiter. 'If you don't mind my saying so, you look far too happy for someone who's supposed to be drowning her sorrows.'

Lorna Carrington laughed softly. 'I suppose I was going through a fairly rough patch last time we met. How about you, though?' Her gaze was shrewdly appraising. 'You got a rotten deal with Halliday's, but didn't you say it had all worked out quite well, after all?'

Kate reached for her glass and sipped her juice, resisting the temptation to look at her watch. For some reason, she half expected to see Luke Redmond striding across the restaurant towards her, and the thought sent a spasm of panic running through her.

'As a matter of fact, we got the contract with Poseidon to redesign the new complex. It's going to be a huge project.'

'Well, in that case, we should be having a double celebration.'

'Double?'

Lorna smiled. 'I'm taking over as head of personnel in Birmingham.'

Kate's eyes widened. 'But that's marvellous! Only I thought . . .'

'Yes, I know.' The other woman's laugh held a note of embarrassment. 'You could say I over-reacted to the news that I was being transferred. I suppose I, of all people, should have known better, but you know what it's like. Rumours fly, and before you know it things are blown up out of all proportion. I guess I fell into the trap of doing just that.'

'Obviously something's happened to change your mind.'

Lorna twirled her glass. 'I think the phrase is—meaningful talks were held with senior management.'

Kate sat back, helping herself to a bread roll. 'I take it you mean Luke Redmond?'

'Well, they certainly don't come any more senior.'

Kate gave an impatient sigh. 'And I suppose he talked you into it?'

'Actually,' Lorna chuckled, 'he talked me *out* of it. I'd gone so far as to hand in my notice. Looking back on it now, I realise it was a pretty stupid thing to do. He might have taken me at my word!'

'As I recall, you had very good grounds,' Kate said

drily. 'You'd been with Halliday's for what? Fifteen years? At least half of those in a pretty senior capacity.'

'Pretty well a lifetime, by some standards,' Lorna quipped gently, and Kate shot her a questioning look.

'I seem to remember last time we met that you weren't exactly taken with the idea of having to uproot and move to Birmingham. In fact, I got the distinct impression that Birmingham was closely akin, in your mind, to the end of the world.'

Lorna grinned. 'I will admit the idea did lack a certain appeal.'

Kate sat back and they waited in silence as their lunch arrived. 'And now it doesn't?'

'Well, it does rather put a different perspective on things that I shall be going there as head of a department which is responsible for roughly three times the number of staff I dealt with at Halliday's.'

'It certainly sounds good.'

'I know.' Lorna smiled over her glass. 'When I think how I stormed into Luke's office, fully prepared to air a list of grievances and with my resignation already typed out . . . You know, I came pretty close to making what could have been the worst mistake of my life. I made a lot of assumptions, quite groundless assumptions as it turned out, not only about the job, but about the man himself.'

Kate's mouth tightened. 'I wonder if the people who were made redundant share your renewed faith?'

'Oh, there were redundancies, I'll admit,' Lorna agreed. 'But in the event they were mainly staff who were due to retire on various grounds anyway, and they all went with a more than generous pension which, to give him his due, I didn't have to negotiate. Most of the others were offered employment elsewhere within the company on compatible terms, and those who couldn't or chose not to go for whatever reason have been amply compensated. A few like myself, actually got a promotion. So, all in all, things were not quite what they may at first have seemed.'

Kate put down her knife and fork, suddenly realising that her appetite had vanished. 'It sounds as if he's done a remarkable sales job,' she said peevishly.

'Oh, I don't think there was any question of a sales job. I'm not saying I don't think he could be quite devastatingly ruthless if the need arose,' Lorna admitted softly, 'but if I'm honest about it I knew Halliday's couldn't go on as they had been doing. Mike must have guessed long before I did that the cards were probably on the table, but he was in the somewhat invidious position of not being able to say anything for fear of causing panic as much as anything.'

'So what it comes down to is survival of the strongest?'

Lorna shrugged. 'Poseidon are a big organisation. They have the finances and they know what it takes to succeed, and you can't do that without a certain element of ruthlessness creeping in. It's a competitive world out there, you know.'

Kate stared down at her plate, making a pretence at eating her food. 'And what about Mike? Where does he fit into all this?'

'To be honest,' Lorna frowned, 'I don't think anyone finds it easy to talk to Mike at the moment. He's in a permanently foul mood, but he adamantly refuses to discuss it. I know, I've tried and nearly had my head bitten off for my pains. Actually, I thought he might have said something to you.'

Kate swallowed hard. 'Not a great deal, except that it looks as if he may be transferred up north.'

'That's news to me.' Lorna raised dark eyebrows. 'But then, as I said, Mike isn't exactly communicative these days.' She looked at her plate, pushing the fish around with her fork. 'I know that he and Luke don't always see eye to eye.'

Kate moistened dry lips. 'Do you know why?'

Lorna shrugged. 'Some clashes of personality are almost inevitable, but Mike's no fool, he must know when he can't win.'

'Even if he's right?' Kate threw in defensively.

'But we don't know that, do we? All I can say is, I hope they settle their differences, whatever they may be, otherwise he may be better off elsewhere.'

Kate's startled gaze rose. 'You mean with another company?'

'It may come to it.'

'He may not see it that way.'

'No, but then neither did I, to begin with. One thing's for sure,' Lorna insisted firmly, 'there's only one boss at Poseidon.'

'And you don't mind working for him?'

'He's fair,' Lorna said lightly. 'Not always sweet-tempered. I'll even go so far as to say he's been like a bear with a sore head of late, but then, under the circumstances, I'd probably be the same.'

Colour darkened Kate's cheeks. 'What circumstances?'

'Well, I don't think I could handle the kind of responsibility he has, could you?'

'I'd say rearranging other people's lives is something he probably takes in his stride.' Kate's smile was derisive.

'I was thinking more that it must make for a pretty lonely life-style.'

Luke Redmond, lonely? The image was totally alien, but Kate felt her heart give an oddly dull thud. 'That doesn't exactly fit the picture I've had,' she said drily. 'In fact, I'm surprised he has time for empire-building.'

'The reports on his private life coud be grossly exaggerated, you know. Besides, he's half-Greek.'

'Is that supposed to prove a point?' Kate said.

Lorna shrugged, sitting back as the waiter brought their coffee. 'I thought Greek men were supposed to hold remarkably strict moral views where their women were concerned. Aren't they supposed to save themselves for marriage? The women, that is?'

'Trust a man to come up with double standards like that,' Kate said acidly.

'Don't they still arrange these things over there? Marriages, I mean.'

Kate felt her hand shake as she stirred cream into her coffee, wondering with a sudden jolt of shock why it had never occurred to her before now that Luke might be engaged or even married. It could explain a lot of things, she realised now; like, for instance, the fact that even in the most fiery moments of passion he had never once spoken the word 'love'.

She felt the colour drain from her face. 'Surely we would have heard if he had a wife?'

'You're probably right,' Lorna conceded indifferently. 'Unless he's the sort of man who likes to keep his private life strictly separate from his business. I can see that for certain men it could have its advantages.'

Kate swallowed the sudden, painful tightness in her throat, and forced a smile. 'I hate to break things up, but I really have to get back.' She reached for her bag, but Lorna waved away her attempt to take the bill.

'So must I, and this is my treat. I'm glad you could make it. I didn't want to leave without saying goodbye and wishing you the best of luck. With the design project,' she added, seeing the look of confusion in Kate's face. 'And don't forget, I shall expect an invitation to the official opening.'

'Don't worry, I won't forget.'

They walked out of the restaurant into the heat of the afternoon, and to pavements dampened by a recent shower of rain. Yet, in spite of it, Kate felt cold.

Climbing into the taxi which took her back to the office, she sat stiff and white, battling against a sudden crazy urge to burst into tears.

She drew an angry breath, telling herself she was behaving like a fool. After all, what Luke Redmond did with his private life was no concern of hers. But there was surprisingly little comfort in the knowledge that she had managed to escape becoming just another name on his list of sexual conquests!

* * *

She was hard at work at her desk when Sue returned to the office. Engrossed in the layout she was working on, Kate didn't look up as Sue collapsed into a chair.

'How did it go?'

'Would you rather I was gentle with you?' Sue eased herself out of her jacket and inspected the contents of the coffee-pot on a tray on the desk. 'Or shall I give it to you straight?'

Kate sat up, gave the other girl a long, steady look, then leaned forwards to press the buzzer on the intercom. 'Jenny, bring some more coffee, will you?' Sitting back, she carefully eased the panic from her eyes. 'I think you'd better tell me about it. Do I take it he refused to see you?'

'Oh, no, he saw me,' Sue conceded wryly. 'As a matter of fact, he was utterly charming, and even took me out for a very nice lunch—which, under the circumstances, I thought was rather generous of him.'

Kate pressed her lips into a thin line. 'What about the report?'

'I gave it to him, and he accepted it.'

Kate ran a distracted hand through her hair. 'Accepted it? What exactly does that mean? Did he say anything, express an opinion?'

Sue threw her a derisive look. 'That was a pretty hefty report. You didn't seriously expect him to sit there and read it there and then, surely?'

'No, of course I didn't expect him to go through it from cover to cover.' Kate gave a sigh of exasperation. 'But did he at least look at it?'

'Actually—no.'

Kate waited. 'So what did he do with it?'

'Well, since you want me to be specific,' Sue glanced hesitantly at her, 'he dropped it into a drawer.'

'Dropped it . . . You mean, that was all? He didn't even comment?'

'To be perfectly honest, I suspect that anything he might have said would be totally unrepeatable. He was definitely not amused. In fact, I got the distinct impression that, had you been within striking distance, your life wouldn't have been worth a great deal.' Sue glanced up as Jenny brought in the coffee, thanked her and poured two cups. 'It was a mistake, me going in your place. *His* words, not mine.'

Kate took a deep breath. 'You did explain that I already had a prior engagement, one I couldn't break?'

'Believe me, I used every ounce of personal charm I possess.'

Kate frowned. 'And what did he say?'

Sue shot her a dubious look. 'He said—and I quote, in so far as the bounds of decency allow—that he is paying handsomely for your services and, without wishing in any way to denigrate my own feelings of loyalty to you, either he gets your undivided attention or the whole deal is off!'

Kate sat back breathing deeply. 'He can't do that!'

'I'm afraid I wouldn't count on it. He suggested that if you had any doubts you could always check the small print. He also told me to say that, when you're ready to talk, you'll know where to reach him. Silence will be interpreted as meaning that you accept termination of the contract.'

Kate's mouth tightened. She didn't doubt for one

moment that he was enjoying every second of his superiority, and the galling thing was that she had played directly into his hands. Her actions deceptively calm, she reached for the phone. 'All right, I'll call him.'

'He's unavailable for the rest of the day.'

Kate's hand dropped from the receiver and she rose to her feet. 'It's probably just as well. What I have to say to Mr Redmond will take a little planning.' She moved to the window, her slim hips emphasised by the well-cut skirt which flared against her calves. 'You say he took you to lunch?'

'It seemed like a good opportunity to try and salvage something out of the wreckage, so I accepted his invitation,' Sue said lightly. 'As a matter of fact, I rather enjoyed it.'

'I'm surprised you had anything in common,' Kate said tightly.

'Actually, we got on surprisingly well. We talked about some of the jewellery design I've done in the past, and somehow got on to cosmetic packaging. He seemed genuinely interested.'

'It's hardly his line, I'd have thought.'

'Neither would I, to begin with, but funnily enough, once he'd put forward some ideas, I could see the relevance, and he does know what he's talking about, Kate. Look at this, for instance.' Sue reached for a sketch-pad, flipping through the pages. 'We got to talking about a whole range of cosmetics—you know, soaps, shampoos, aftershaves.'

Kate stared out of the window trying to blot out the memory of one all too memorable aftershave. 'Don't tell me he's planning to take over from the Avon ladies!'

'If he did,' Sue chuckled, 'I, for one, wouldn't mind having him turn up on my doorstep. Seriously though, we were talking about packaging, and he suddenly came up with the idea of possibly bringing out a whole new range of toiletries which would be exclusive to Poseidon. You know the sort of things, most hotels provide little sachets of bath foam and guest soap. It's a fabulous idea, Kate. You have to give him some credit.'

Sue's enthusiasm seemed to engender a deep resentment in her which she knew to be unreasonable. 'It sounds as if it could be an expensive project.'

'I pointed that out, but he asked me to go ahead and produce some ideas.' Sue grinned. 'It was as much as I could do not to start sketching on the tablecloth.' Her mouth twisted into a smile. 'Don't you think there's just a chance you might be misjudging him, Kate? I mean, I don't know what went on between you two, but, whatever it was, somewhere along the line you both seem to have taken a wrong turning.'

Kate stiffened warily. 'I may have no choice about working for him, but to the best of my knowledge there's nothing in the contract which stipulates that I'm obliged to like him.'

Sue threw her a look of frustration and rose to her feet. 'Well, at least I tried.' She paused at the door. 'Just take some advice. Don't push him too far, unless you're prepared to have him retaliate.'

Kate flushed angrily. 'Slavery was abolished over a hundred years ago.'

'That wasn't exactly what I had in mind.' Sue sighed.

'Well, I really don't need a lecture in psychology, and in any case aren't you jumping to some rather groundless conclusions?'

'Am I?'

Kate frowned. 'His sort have *women*—plural—and frankly I don't fancy being just another name on the list.'

'It obviously bothers you that he even considers the idea,' Sue smiled wryly. 'Hasn't it ever occurred to you to wonder why he's so persistent?'

'No, because I already know the answer. As far as he's concerned, the conquest is all that counts.'

'You know, for an intelligent woman, there are times when I despair of you, Kate Langley. I mean, have you never thought there could be another reason?'

'Yes, it has. His ego would never allow that anyone could possibly turn him down.'

'Oh, come on!' Sue had to laugh, despite the seriousness of the situation. 'Luke Redmond doesn't need to chase women. He could take his pick.'

Kate's mouth tightened. 'So what are you trying to say?'

'Are you in love with him?' queried Sue softly, watching the colour fluctuate in the other girl's cheeks.

Kate's body tensed visibly. 'I don't even *like* the man.'

'I don't think that really answers the questions, if you don't mind my saying so.' Sue frowned. 'It's not so terrible, you know.'

Kate's smile was strained. 'It's not so terrible because I don't intend to let it happen. Luke Redmond's only interest in me is in proving that I'm exactly like all the rest. Oh, I'm sure the fact that I've resisted has probably added to his determination, but I know precisely how long his interest would last. Just the time it takes for another woman to walk into his life.' Her eyes narrowed. 'Well, that's not for me.'

Sue shook her head. 'I happen to think you're completely wrong about him, but I can take a hint.' She opened the door. 'Don't forget to phone him. I'm off now, but perhaps we can kick over a few ideas for these sketches tomorrow.'

'Fine. I'm in the office for the rest of the day. I might even do some work on them tonight.' Anything in fact, Kate thought, which would take her mind off a seemingly ever-encroaching awareness of Luke Redmond . . .

CHAPTER EIGHT

THERE was still an oppressive threat of thunder in the air as Kate let herself into the flat, and she immediately set about flinging open the windows to let out the heat.

In a daze of tiredness, she stripped and showered, changing into a cool cotton nightie and satin wrap before making herself a cup of coffee and a sandwich.

By the time darkness had fallen, she had passed the phone so many times, only to put off the final moment of contact, that when she finally forced herself to dial Luke's number her hand was actually shaking with tension.

Some part of her had still held out the faint hope that he would be out, so that when he answered tersely at the very first ring it needed every ounce of will-power she possessed not to slam the phone down again.

He had obviously been sitting by the phone— waiting for her call. Kate moistened her lips awkwardly.

'Luke, this is Kate.'

There was a moment of silence before he said curtly, 'Isn't it a little late? I imagined you must have gone to bed by now.'

She drew a deep breath. 'It's not that late. Anyway,

I've been rather busy.'

'So I gather,' he bit out grimly. 'I trust you enjoyed your lunch?'

'Yes, as a matter of fact, I did.' Kate bit at her lower lip. 'That's why I called.'

'To let me know how much you enjoyed your lunch?'

She stiffened at the edge of sarcasm in his voice. 'That wasn't what I meant, and you know it. I . . . I rang to explain why I couldn't meet you today.'

'I'm really not interested in excuses,' he rasped. 'Your partner already spoke nobly in your defence. I hope she gets some sort of reward for her loyalty.'

'They weren't excuses,' Kate snapped. 'She was telling the truth. I already had a prior engagement which I wasn't prepared to break in order to fit in with what was a purely arbitrary arrangement on your part.'

'There is nothing arbitrary about a contract, Kate.'

'It doesn't give you the right to behave unreasonably.'

'On the contrary,' he said softly, 'it gives me the right to do exactly as I please where Poseidon's interests are concerned, and that includes the right to insist upon your personal and undivided attention whenever and wherever I think necessary.' There was a fractional pause. 'Of course, if you're not prepared to accept the terms, I can always cancel the contract.'

Kate gritted her teeth. 'You can't do that.'

'I think you'll find I can,' he taunted softly.

'I'll sue for breach of contract.'

'Then you'll lose,' he told her. 'I suggest you

read the small print, Kate. It says, I give the orders, you obey.'

She drew a deep, controlling breath. 'You may have brought my services in a business capacity,' her tone was cold and formal, 'but don't make the mistake of thinking that gives you any rights where my personal life is concerned, because it doesn't.'

For a fleeting second, she wished she could see his expression, then blushed as he drawled softly, 'Still fighting, Kate?'

She swallowed hard. 'Just making my feelings perfectly clear, so that there can be no possible misunderstanding.'

'Oh, I don't think that's very likely, do you? I'm sure I know your feelings—intimately.'

She blushed a fiery red. 'I won't be blackmailed.'

'Is that what you think I'm doing?'

'Well, isn't it?'

'I don't see it that way, Kate.'

'No, of course you don't,' she snapped. 'You simply indulge in a little coercion.'

'Only when absolutely necessary.'

Her mouth tightened as she sensed that he was deliberately provoking an argument she would never win. 'What about the report?'

'What about the report?'

'Can we stop playing games?' she said flatly. 'We both know what this is all about. When do you wish to see me?'

'We had an appointment several hours ago,' he ground harshly, 'which *you* failed to keep.'

'I have explained,' she said impatiently. 'Surely we

can come to some new arrangement?'

'Unfortunately, it isn't convenient for me to do that right now. In any case, I'm not in the habit of rescheduling my appointments once they're made.' His voice opened up a chasm between them.

'Then what do you want me to do?'

'I somehow doubt that you need my advice as to how you conduct your life.'

She flushed sensing his mockery. 'That wasn't what I meant. I was talking about the report . . .'

'When I've read it and come up with some conclusions, I'll be in touch.'

Angry colour suffused her cheeks. 'Yes, but . . .'

'You'll hear from me, Kate,' he ground out. 'Right now, it isn't convenient. I'm expecting an important call.'

Her mouth twisted. 'From a lady, no doubt.'

'As a matter of fact, yes. Does that make you feel any better, Kate?'

She drew in a sharp breath, wondering why the cool admission should shake her. 'I . . . I'm sorry. I had no right . . .'

'What's the matter, Kate? Surely you can't be jealous?'

'Why, you . . .' She heard his quiet laughter, and it was several seconds before she realised the phone had gone dead. Shaking with anger, she replaced the receiver. He was paying her back, of course, deliberately making her wait, knowing what the uncertainty would do to her. But as for being jealous . . . the very idea was ludicrous. Or, at least, only days ago that would have been true!

She wasn't aware of the tears coursing down her cheeks until the doorbell rang, and she blinked, dazedly. Now, who could that be? She certainly wasn't expecting anyone. Brushing the evidence of her distress away, she went to open the door.

'Mike!'

'Hi.' He stood frowning uncertainly at her. 'I know it's late, but I had to see you.' His gaze went past her, and his expression became guarded. 'I haven't called at a bad time, have I? I mean, you're not . . .?'

'I don't have a visitor, Mike, if that's what you mean.' She held the door wider. 'Why don't you come in? Unless you feel that your being here at this time of night might be misinterpreted?'

Mike had the grace to flush. 'I guess I deserved that.'

'I'd say so.' She moved away, switching on another lamp, purposely not asking him to sit. 'Isn't it a little late to be making social calls?' She hadn't intended the contempt in her voice to seem quite so obvious, but it found its mark.

He stood uncertainly, clearly shaken by her coolness. 'To be honest, I hadn't realised what time it was. I guess it's taken me a while to pluck up the courage.'

Kate frowned. 'To do what?'

'To apologise.' He gave her a direct look. 'I know it's probably not much comfort, I can't take back the things I said, but I want you to know that I realise now I may have jumped to a few conclusions.'

She frowned, trying to sympathise with the uneasy figure he made. 'I take it you mean you realise they were unfounded?'

Mike shrugged. 'I guess I had no right to pass judgement.'

'No, you're right, you didn't,' Kate fumed. 'So why do I get the impression that's precisely what you're doing?'

His mouth tightened. 'You're not making this easy, Kate.'

'I'm glad to hear it!' Her eyes narrowed. 'I'm still not even sure exactly what it is you're trying to say.'

'I just wanted you to know that I realise I had no claim on you, and that what you choose to do with your private life is none of my business.'

'In other words,' she said with restrained anger, 'you haven't actually come here to apologise. What you're saying is that you're generously prepared to overlook my indiscretions?' She faced him, bristling with anger now. 'I think perhaps you'd better leave. We both seem to have said all there is to say.'

Mike stood his ground. 'Oh, hell! Look, you're twisting everything I'm trying to say.'

'Am I?' she demanded. 'Well, in that case, you're probably not saying it loudly or clearly enough.'

He dug his hands in his pockets. 'That's probably because I'm not finding it easy. Damn it, Kate, I came to say that I'm leaving and, whether you believe it or not, I'm going to miss you. I'm beginning to think I made a mistake in coming, only I didn't want to go without saying goodbye, that's all.'

'You're leaving?' Her face paled. 'Mike, you're not . . .'

'No,' he said quickly. 'I'm not being sent up north,

after all.' He threw her a wary look. 'It seems the powers-that-be have decided I can be of more use elsewhere. I don't know what—or who—persuaded them to change their minds, but I'm grateful.'

She swallowed hard. 'So what will you be doing?'

'I've been reassigned as manager of one of the other hotels in the chain, with direct responsibility for bringing it into line with Poseidon's policy for redevelopment and for retraining staff.'

'But that's marvellous!' Her thoughts flew to Luke, and her colour deepened as she remembered the exchange they had had on this very subject. 'I'm glad it's worked out, and things aren't as bad as you thought.'

'I'm glad, too.' When Mike took her in his arms, she offered no resistance. 'As a matter of fact, I was rather hoping you'd think about going with me. It could still work, you know. Between us, I mean.'

'I don't think so, Mike,' she said awkwardly. 'We're good friends, and that has meant a lot to me.'

'To me, too. But I'd thought it would go quite a way beyond just friendship, Kate. You surely must have realised that?'

She shook her head, detaching herself gently from his arms. 'I'm sorry, Mike, I can't honestly say it did. I'd always assumed, perhaps naïvely, that marriage required a certain element of trust.'

'Oh, hell!' His mouth twisted. 'I guess I deserve that, too.'

'No.' She shook her head. 'I'm sorry.'

'It's Redmond, isn't it?'

Her eyes darkened. 'Not the way you think.'

'I'm not that naïve, Kate. He's got to you. I just
hope you realise you're playing with fire. His sort
don't stick to the rules—they make their own up as
they go along, and I'd hate to see you get hurt.'

Kate drew a ragged breath. 'I appreciate your
concern, truly.'

'You know it's more than that,' he said softly. 'If
ever you change your mind, or need a shoulder to cry
on . . .'

'You'll have to write and let me have your address.'
She wished he would go. Above all, she hoped he
wouldn't kiss her, forcing her to make comparisons.

'There's still time to change your mind and come
with me.'

'It's a nice thought, but it wouldn't work.' She
forced a smile. 'You've got a whole new future
opening up, and I have a contract which has to be
honoured.'

'Contracts can be broken.'

She flushed. 'Not this one. Besides, you don't
need . . .'

'Don't say it,' he prompted gently. 'As for the
bright new future—well, that may be just a little
optimistic.'

'What do you mean?'

He shrugged. 'Just that the new job is on a
temporary basis to start with.' He fixed her with a
discerning eye. 'It's been made fairly clear that I'm on
trial. I thought you'd know.'

'No, I didn't.' She frowned, aware of the pulse
thudding in her throat. 'But you'll be all right.'

Mike raised an eyebrow. 'I'd say that rather

depends, wouldn't you?' He reached out to touch her cheek. 'It looks as if we've both got to be on our best behaviour. I'd wish you luck, but I suspect it's not going to be luck that counts, is it, Kate?'

CHAPTER NINE

IN THE space of a week, summer had vanished and
autumn set in with a vengeance.

Seated at the desk, Kate reached for her briefcase
and took out a buff file. After giving it several
seconds' consideration, she opened a drawer and
dropped it inside. She had worked solidly all weekend
on an idea, making sketches, matching colours,
grabbing a sandwich and a cup of coffee rather that let
herself be diverted while the design seemed to be
flowing. And it had paid off. Kate didn't indulge in
false modesty. When a piece of work was good,
whether her own or anyone elses, she acknowledged
it, confident in her own judgement.

Flicking the switch on the electric kettle which she
kept in the office precisely for the times when she
needed to get on undisturbed, Kate made herself a cup
of instant coffee and went back to her desk.

She sat back, glancing over the list of messages
Jenny had placed strategically on her blotting pad. 'M
and L rang to ask if you would care to attend the
official opening of their new office equipment design
centre next week. Cheese and wine will be served.
Strictly informal.' And a salesman behind every
potted plant, order book at the ready! Smiling, Kate
reached for her pen and wrote, 'No—make suitable

excuses.' She studied the next message. 'Secretary, St Helen's, rang to confirm your talk on colour and modern living to senior girls. J and S apologise for delay in despatching fabric samples. Production difficulties on that particular batch of colours. Is alternative acceptable?'

'No!' Kate frowned as she wrote briskly. 'Remind them that we have a deadline. Tell them, if they can't produce, we go elsewhere.'

It wasn't the first time they had had difficulty with this particular supplier, and she made a mental note to talk to Sue about transferring their account elsewhere in any case.

Her gaze ran to the bottom of the list. 'One obscene phone call. I advised caller seek immediate medical help. Apart from that, only minor queries. Letters for signing in folder.'

But nothing from Luke. In a week, not as much as a letter or a phone call. Kate rose restlessly, pushing her chair back and crossing to the window to watch the rain lashing on to the street below. The weather was cold and depressing. Like her mood, she thought, feeling anger begin to build up. The trouble was, he could afford to play a waiting game. *He* had nothing to lose, whereas she stood to lose a great deal, in more senses than one!

She went back to her desk, telling herself resolutely that she would put him firmly out of her mind. Except that it was easier said than done when the mere thought of him seemed to exert a depressing power over her ragged emotions.

She was engrossed in a column of figures when Sue breezed into the office, the bright cerise of her ski pants and jacket bringing a refreshing burst of colour into a drab morning.

'Hi, another bright new day full of joy and promise.'

Kate threw her a scathing look. 'Well, I'm glad someone's feeling cheerful.' She glanced up from the letter she was signing.

'It's the only way.' Sue slipped into the chair. 'You're a fool to yourself, Kate Langley. Martyrs get their reward in heaven. I prefer mine now.'

Kate broke into laughter. 'You're incorrigible!'

'Not me.' Sue waved a hand deprecatingly. 'I just like to draw a line between my social and business life. You should try it some time. For instance, why not come over to my place one evening for a meal?' She threw a shrewd glance at the pale features. 'I may not be the world's best cook, but I can just about throw together a reasonable curry. How about it?'

Kate was thrown by the suggestion. 'Well, yes, OK, I'd love to. But how about . . . Keith, is it?'

'Don't worry about him.' Sue dismissed her live-in lover with a grin. 'It won't hurt him to listen to a little girl-talk once in a while. Anyway, I'm planning a party. My sister and her husband are bringing the kids over from Australia for a visit. I'd like you to meet them.'

Kate lowered her gaze, feeling that she was being drawn into things she wasn't in any mood to enjoy. 'Just give me plenty of notice, will you?'

Sue wasn't fooled. 'Diary's that full, huh?'

Kate reached for another letter. 'So that I can buy something presentable to wear. It seems ages since I bought anything.'

'You don't exactly go anywhere.' Sue broke off, embarrassed suddenly. 'Hey, look, I'm sorry.'

'That's all right,' Kate said evenly. 'It happens to be true, and it's high time I did something about it.' She fell silent, faced with the realisation tht it *was* true that, though her wardrobe was extensive, most of the items in it had all been purchased during the past five years with the sole purpose of suitability to her working life in mind. She had gone for quality, with an eye to fashion, but for a long time there had been nothing even remotely frivolous. Functional, sensible and safe were the words which sprang to mind as she caught sight of herself in the mirror she had purposely fixed to the back of the door in order that she could always check her appearance before leaving to attend business meetings.

It showed her now, a tall, slim figure in a calf-length skirt which flared gently as she moved, and a high-necked blouse to which she had fastened a tiny turquoise brooch, picked up years ago on a stall at a country market fair.

Over the back of her chair was draped the jacket which matched the skirt. Her shoes were black, high-heeled court shoes. To the objective onlookers, the effect would have been stunning. To Kate, the words predictable and safe said it all. But then she swept the thought aside; she was here to do a job, and the image went with the job.

She came out of her reverie and reached for a file. 'I came up with an idea over the weekend. I'd like to know what you think. It's a shopping gallery to be included in the Poseidon project.' She spread the pages out. 'How about coffee?'

'Best offer I've had today—so far.' Sue leaned forward, glanced at the pages, then sat back.

Kate buzzed the intercom. 'Jenny, can we have coffee, please? Oh, and I've signed the letters. I'll get to the calls later, unless something urgent has come in?' She despised herself for the tiny flicker of hope as she said it.

'No, nothing new.' There was a slight pause before Jenny said, 'Do you want me to get Poseidon International?'

For a second, Kate almost weakened. 'No, thanks, Jen.'

'OK, I'll bring in the coffee.'

Kate swivelled her chair back to the desk, hoping she had sufficiently schooled her features for her frustration not to show. She was on the defensive and knew it. She sat back. 'What do you think?'

Sue looked up from the file. 'I'd say you're going to have to make the first move and call him if you're really so desperate to know what he thinks of the report.'

A taut smile flickered on Kate's face as Jenny brought in the tray of coffee. 'Thanks, Jen.' She waited until the girl had left before returning to the subject. 'I was talking about the sketches.'

'Oh, I see, sorry. They're good, but you don't need me to tell you that. In any case, I'm not the one you have to sell the idea to.'

'I'd still appreciate your opinion.' Kate poured out the coffee, handed over Sue's, and carried her own back to her chair. 'Do you think the gallery idea could work?'

'I think it's great, and why not? It would give the hotel an edge. Tourists like to shop. Why shouldn't they be able to buy things like cosmetics and souvenirs right there on the premises?' She leaned forward, turning one of the pages. 'You've shown three units.'

'That's right. One to carry the range of products you'll be designing exclusively for the Poseidon name—cosmetics, toiletries and so on. One would take a range of books, magazines, stationery, and the other possibly a small but select range of clothes, accessories, bags and so on. I'm not talking on a huge scale. Space would be a consideration, for one thing, and expense for another.'

'I take it you've sounded Luke out on the idea?'

Kate jabbed the top on her pen. 'Just the basics in the report.'

'So,' Sue nodded towards the phone, 'ring him. After all, it's been a week.'

Kate snuffed out a disturbing image of Luke's self-satisfied expression if she were to give in and make the call. It would be playing directly into his hands, and yet—her mouth tightened—what other choice did she have? Anything was better than this uncertainty.

She blinked hard, erasing the image and sighed wearily. 'I'll phone him later.' Reclaiming her pen, she lowered her head over the figures she had been working on, barely acknowledging Sue's wave of farewell. But once the door had closed she gave up all pretence at concentration.

Pushing her chair back, she paced restlessly to the window again, conscious of a tight knot of tension in her stomach. The mere thought of having to pick up the phone, with all its connotations of submission, suddenly made her blood boil. He had *planned* it. This was his way of teaching her a lesson, and he had certainly wasted no time about it, she thought bitterly, remembering his admission that he had been waiting for a call from another woman. One of many, she didn't doubt. Luke Redmond wasn't a man to accept rejection without offering some retaliation. He had to be the master. But where would that need to prove his superiority end? The thought sent a quick shaft of panic running through her as she returned to the desk, reached for the phone and dialled an outside line.

Within seconds, a voice answered. 'Poseidon International. Can I help you?'

'Yes.' Kate forced herself to take deep, even breaths. 'I wish to speak to Mr Redmond. Mr Luke Redmond.'

There was a muffled pause at the other end of the line, as if the speaker had covered the phone. Kate waited, tapping her pen on the desk.

'Hello, caller, I'll put you through to Mr Redmond's personal secretary.'

'But I don't wish to speak to his personal secretary,' Kate snapped. 'I asked for Mr Redmond—in person.' She swallowed hard. 'Tell him it's Mrs Langley. Kate Langley.'

'I'm sorry, Mrs Langley, but all Mr Redmond's calls have to be directed through his secretary.'

'But this is urgent—and personal,' she ground out.

'I do understand, caller.' An audible sigh accompanied the words. 'I'm putting you through now.'

Kate's hand shook, then tightened, as a different but unmistakably female voice came on the line.

Kate closed her eyes. She was going mad.

'May I help you?' the voice prompted gently.

Kate's own voice sounded unnatural, trapped somewhere in her throat. 'I've already explained that I need to speak to Mr Redmond—in person.'

'Yes, Mrs Langley.' The voice was mature, soothing and infinitely patient. 'I do understand. Unfortunately, I'm afraid Mr Redmond isn't available. This is Margaret Foster, his personal secretary, speaking.'

Kate's lips tightened as if to stifle the scream that was welling up inside her. Not again! It couldn't be happening again. 'Perhaps you can tell me when he *will* be available?'

'I'm terribly sorry, Mrs Langley. Right now, I really can't say. I'm afraid Mr Redmond is away.'

Kate's heart lurched painfully in her breast. 'But . . . I was expecting him to call me. Surely you must have some idea as to when he's due back?'

'Unfortunately, no, I haven't. He left rather suddenly, and his plans were a little uncertain.'

Kate bit at her lower lip. 'Yes, I see, but I was expecting an urgent call from him about a report.'

'I don't think you should worry about it, Mrs Langley. I understand that in his absence everything connected with the new project is being handled by our head office in Athens.'

'Athens!'

'Yes, I know,' Margaret Foster's amusement was evident, even over the phone. 'It does rather bring a whole new meaning to the word commuting, although it's part of Poseidon's company policy that senior managers attend annual conventions abroad on a pretty regular basis, and I'm quite sure Mr Redmond has kept our Athens people fully informed. As a matter of fact, he was in touch with them shortly before he left, and I received a telex from him earlier today instructing me to book you on the earliest possible flight out to Greece. I was going to phone you with the details later, when I'd confirmed them.'

Taking a deep breath, Kate sat down. 'You mean . . . they want *me* to go to Athens?'

'Yes, I know.' Margaret Foster sounded vaguely troubled. 'It is rather short notice, but I have managed to get a ticket for the flight leaving the day after tomorrow, and I understand that you'll be meeting our co-owner, Mr Andreas Kiriakides. Unfortunately, I can't confirm the precise time, but you'll be given more information when you reach Athens.' There was a momentary pause. 'I do hope this isn't going to be terribly awkward. You can make the flight? Only I believe there is some question of urgency.'

Foraging in the desk drawer for her diary, Kate fought for self-control. Pencilling quickly through the appointments already listed there, she scrawled a quick note for Sue. 'As it happens, I can probably rearrange things. I take it it would only be for a brief stay?'

'Oh, I imagine you could safely make that assumption. Mrs Langley. The date on the return flight was left open. I'll have it sent round to you by special messenger.'

'You appear to have thought of everything,' Kate said drily.

'Alas, I can't really take credit for that. Mr Redmond thought of everything. I'm simply carrying out his instructions.'

'I see.' Kate's mouth twisted. 'And in the event that I might not have . . . found it convenient, I suppose there was some contingency plan?'

There was a slight pause before Margaret Foster laughed. 'Do you know, I don't believe it even occurred to him. How like a man!'

How like this particular man! Kate thought, her blood boiling. But then, Luke Redmond knew he held all the cards. The one consoling thought in the whole affair was that, two days from now, she would be out of the country and out of his reach. Yet somehow, even that thought failed to offer the comfort she had hoped for since, though in reality she might be several thousand miles away, in her dreams there were no barriers and no defences. He had said she couldn't run away for ever, her lips quirked. But at least this time she had a head start!

CHAPTER TEN

ATHENS lazed in the shimmering white afternoon heat, an inelegant sprawl of ancient and modern, edged by the sparkling sapphire depths of the Aegean.

To Kate, seated in the black limousine which had met her at the airport, there was something of a dream-like quality about it all as she sat back, feasting her eyes on the drowsy city.

The colourful awnings of roadside cafés flapped gently in a sticky breeze. Sponge sellers ambled along the tree-lined boulevards, waiting for the tourists who were their living. In the tiny, flower-filled square, businessmen and pretty, dark-eyed girls sat drinking coffee.

Kate fanned her cheeks, finding almost no relief, despite the car's open windows. After a four-hour flight and the chaos at the airport, what she wanted more than anything right now was a long, cool shower and a cup of tea—not necessarily in that order.

As the car turned a bend in the road, Kate swung her head to stare at the scene behing them, and gave an audible gasp of wonderment as the sun sparkled on the distant sea.

The driver smiled. 'This is your first visit to Athens?'

Kate turned to meet his gaze in the driving mirror.

'Not just to Athens, to Greece.' She blushed slightly, aware that he had been watching her reactions. 'I don't know what I expected. I knew it would be beautiful, but not quite so . . . spectacular.'

He laughed. 'Athens——' one hand left the wheel to gesture dismissively '—is not Greece. I give you my card—you wish to go sightsee, you call—I take you.'

Kate smiled. 'I'd like that very much, but I'm afraid I'm here on business, not for a holiday.'

He half frowned. 'You take the time. Is a long way to come and not see Greece. I show you best places.'

Kate sat back against the upholstery. 'Don't you work for Poseidon?'

'Poseidon, yes, sometimes.' He grinned, rocking his hand from side to side. 'But I show my friends the sights.' He reached in his trouser pocket and handed a card over his shoulder. 'Keep this. If you wish to see real Greece, not where tourists go, you call. Ask for Spiros.'

Smiling, Kate tucked the card into her bag, knowing she would never use it, but still, she thought as she stared out of the window, there was nothing to prevent her from coming back some day. Except that, in her mind, Greece and Luke had already become disturbingly synonymous. She straightened her shoulders, clamping down forcibly on her thoughts, unaware that a pair of dark eyes watched and wondered what could possibly have caused the faint flush that suddenly darkened the English girl's pretty features.

'You meet friends in Athens? Maybe?'

Kate blinked, and shifted her gaze back to the

window. 'I'm afraid not. I don't expect to be here for more than a few days. Just long enough for a meeting, before I fly back to England.'

'Ah, is a pity . . .'

Kate silently disagreed. It was safer, she thought. The less time she spent here, the less time she had to get to know it, to let it weave its magic. She leaned forward, frowning. 'I didn't expect the streets to be so quiet. I thought there would be more noise, more traffic. And the houses are all shuttered.'

Spiros laughed. 'Only tourists stay in the sun. In afternoons is very hot, eighty, ninety degrees. Greeks stay home and sleep.'

'Ah, you mean it's the siesta.'

'Siesta.' Spiros nodded, grinning. 'Later, when is cooler, shops open again and tavernas, until very late. You want to hear *bouzouki* music, best near Acropolis.' He made a face. 'Too many tourists, but still good.' He looked at his watch. 'Hotel not far now. Is very nice place, maybe best in Athens.' He indicated ahead as the car turned a corner. 'Here is Syntagma.'

The elegant square was lined by large, exclusive hotels, cafés and tall office buildings. Most of them, Kate noticed, belonging to tourist agencies, airlines or business companies. Palm trees bloomed alongside orange trees and cypresses, apparently quite untroubled by traffic fumes.

The car turned yet another corner and slid to a halt. 'Hotel Athena Poseidon.' Spiros leapt out to open the door for Kate. 'I bring bag.'

'That's all right. I only have the one, and it isn't

heavy.' Kate stood on the pavement as he got back into the car and waved.

'OK, don't forget—you call.'

She paused on the steps, briefly appreciating the white building, which was aflame with a riot of colour from hanging flower-baskets and sun-canopies, before making her way into the cool airiness of the hotel's reception area.

A girl working behind the desk smiled as Kate approached her. *'Kalispera.'*

Kate put her bag down. 'Oh dear, I'm sorry, I don't . . .'

'Please,' the girl laughed apologeticaly, 'I speak English. Can I help you?' She frowned, reaching for a ledger. 'I am afraid we have no rooms, *kyria.* You understand, this is our busy season.'

'No, I don't want a room,' Kate hastened to assure her. 'At least . . . I do already have a reservation. The booking was made through Poseidon International in England. The name is Langley, Mrs Kate Langley.'

'Oh, yes. Mrs Langley, I'm so sorry. You are expected.' She pressed a bell located on the desk. 'We have a suite already prepared for you.'

'A suite?' Kate frowned. 'Oh, but I think there must be some mistake. I don't need a suite. A room will be quite sufficient. I really don't expect to be here for long.'

The girl reached for her ledger again in obvious confusion. 'No, there is no mistake. A suite was reserved. I have no other instructions.'

Kate frowned, then shrugged. 'Oh, well, I expect it can all be sorted out in the morning. Right now, I'd very much like to shower and change.'

'Yes, of course, you must be tired after your journey. I'll have someone take your luggage.' She glanced at the solitary bag. 'The rest is to follow?'

'No, I have only the one bag. As I said, I don't expect to be here long.'

The receptionist seemed momentarily taken aback. 'Yes, of course, *Kyria* Langley.' She reached for a key. 'The suite is yours for as long as you wish it, and of course the hotel's facilities are entirely at your disposal.'

'It's a nice thought.' Kate reached for her bag. 'Unfortunately, I doubt that I shall be able to take advantage of them. I'm only here on business, in fact.' She paused. 'I believe I'm supposed to meet a Mr Kiriakides. Perhaps you can tell me if the appointment has been arranged?'

'Ah, yes, I have it here. For nine o'clock tomorrow morning.'

'Thank you.' Kate followed a porter, who led her from the lift to her suite, where he unlocked the door and stood back to allow her to enter.

She did so, making no attempt to conceal a gasp of delight as she walked into a room, fragrant with the perfume of flowers. From the sitting-room, complete with couch, large easy chairs and even a writing-desk, she wandered through to an exquisite bathroom with sunken bath and shower, to a bedroom furnished in deepening shades of pink.

So much luxury, she thought wryly, and so little time to enjoy it. Running a hand experimentally over the large double bed, she banished the fleeting but infinitely disturbing thought that it would make a delightful honeymoon suite.

Breathing hard, she closed the door firmly behind the porter and went straight to the bathroom to douse her burning cheeks with cold water! As far as she and Luke Redmond were concerned, the honeymoon was over even before it had begun! But she was appalled to discover the effect that even the mere thought of him had had on her.

Catching sight of herself in the mirror, she experienced a sense of shock. Her cheeks were flushed and her eyes a dark, stormy green.

Luke Redmond might be thousands of miles away, and for the first time since he had walked into her life she should have felt safe. But somehow safe didn't equate with happy, and when, several hours later, she finally crawled exhausted into the large, empty bed, she was still trying to equate the two—without much success!

Kate stood at the window of the plush penthouse office, staring down at the complex below. The sun was already hot, and several small groups of people were sitting at tables round the pool eating a leisurely breakfast, while a girl in a skimpy, bright yellow bikini was splashing noisily in the water. It was a holidaymaker's paradise. Unfortunately, Kate had to remind herself with a slight pang of envy, she wasn't here on holiday, she was here on business, and once it was concluded she would be on the first flight back to England.

Glancing impatiently at her watch, she forced

herself to sit in the chair and reached into her briefcase for her copy of the report.

She didn't need to study it. The figures were already imprinted on her brain, but knowing them and selling them, selling herself, in a way, to a man she had never even met . . . She was taking what was probably one of the biggest gambles of her life so far, and she was nervous to the point where her hands were actually shaking. For the first time in her life, she wished she had a cigarette—anything to keep them occupied.

Rising to her feet again, she pushed the heavy weight of her hair from her face, already conscious of the slight beading of perspiration on her back. Another five minutes and she would press one of the buzzers on the desk and ask if she had been forgotten.

A minute to nine o'clock. So much for the corridors of power! She could have taken time to enjoy the breakfast of fresh warm croissants and preserves which had been delivered to her suite with her tray of morning coffee, except that when it came to it she had felt too restless to eat. Instead, she had taken a long, cool shower, leaving her damp hair to hang loosely about her shoulders as she dried herself and slipped into pastel-coloured undies and a dress of raw silk.

Just for a second, catching a glimpse of herself in a long mirror, Kate wondered whether she should have chosen to wear something more formal. The pale mint dress, for all it looked simple, seemed to draw out the colour of her eyes, while the neat waist and straight skirt accentuated her slim figure.

Its suitability or otherwise was hardly relevant, she

realised, turning away from her reflection, since it was far too late to do anything about it now in any case.

She was just about to look at her watch again when the door opened and she turned to greet Andreas Kiriakides. Dry-mouthed, tense with nerves, she had actually managed to force her lips into a smile of greeting, before her panicked gaze flew to the tall figure who stood motionless, watching the colour drain from her face as his eyes raked over her.

'Well, aren't you at least going to say you're pleased to see me, Kate?'

Frozen into shocked immobility, she was scarcely aware that he took the hand she still held outstretched as the all too disturbingly familiar voice mocked her gently.

She closed her eyes tight, telling herself it was all a dream—or better still—a nightmare. As her eyelids flew open and she felt the colour burn slowly back into her cheeks, she knew, alas, that it was certainly no dream. Luke Redmond was devastatingly real. '*You!*'

For a few seconds, she stood in numb disbelief before sanity returned, and without even giving herself time to think she had wrenched her hand from his grasp and was heading for the door.

She had actually made it when a hand suddenly gripped her arm, and she was swung round to find herself looking up into Luke's strong features.

'Kate, don't,' he said softly as she struggled in his grasp.

Her eyes blurred, and she took a deep breath before trying to pull herself angrily from his grasp. 'Let me go!'

'I can explain.'

Her green eyes flashed stormily at the hands encircling her wrists. 'Somehow I doubt that. In any case, I really don't want to hear.'

But he didn't let her go. Instead, he closed the door quietly behind her, and she shivered as, with cool deliberation, he drew her towards him. 'I'm not letting you go anywhere until you've calmed down and listened to what I have to say.'

She fumed inwardly as she struggled, only to give up the attempt as his grip merely tightened. Swallowing convulsively, she subsided only to press her hands against his chest, forcing some distance between them as she became aware that, in spite of herself, her body was responding to his nearness.

'This isn't what you think, Kate.'

'You don't know what I think.' Her eyes blazed angrily.

'Maybe not, but I can make a pretty good guess,' he said thickly. 'And I will admit, it probably looks bad.'

Her mouth curled with cynicism. 'You don't know just how bad. I think you planned this. I'd rather not guess at your motives,' she told him, only to gasp as in one swift movement his arms had imprisoned her, tightening round her.

'You'll have to take my word for it that it wasn't planned, Kate. Not like this.' He shook her. 'Do you believe that?'

She must stay calm, she told herself, and felt her blood race as she stared into the sombre dark eyes. 'I . . . I want to believe you, but even you must realise that, under the circumstances, that isn't easy.'

Her heart thudded as the dark eyes, glittering with intensity, looked down into hers. His fingers tightened on her burning skin, and she saw the brief widening of his eyes before he drew her roughly towards him. 'God, I still want you,' he breathed raggedly. 'I told myself I wouldn't let this happen, but it seems I only have to be near you . . .' For a second, the dark eyes smouldered, then she felt the strength of his powerfully muscular body against hers as his mouth came down in a brutal, punishing kiss.

She moaned a faint protest as his tongue invaded her mouth, sending a shaft of unexpected and exquisite pleasure coursing through her veins.

'I didn't plan this,' he said again, his voice muffled against her hair.

At first she tried to fight him, her eyes closing as a feeling of weakness washed over her. This wasn't supposed to be happening, but her responses seemed to be coming from somewhere totally beyond her control.

'Kate, have you any idea how I feel?' he groaned huskily, as his mouth sought and traced the hollow of her neck.

If it was anything like the way she was feeling right now, Kate thought, then she had a pretty good idea! His hand moved, sensuously seeking and caressing her breast until the nipple hardened, like a flower bursting into life.

'You *are* glad to see me,' he muttered hoarsely.

The spell was broken. With a soft cry of protest she wrenched herself out of his arms, her fingers brushing shakily against her mouth, where the pressure of his kiss still seemed to remain. Her hand went out guardedly as he moved towards her. 'Don't touch me!' She blinked hard, uncomfortably aware of the effect he was having on her emotions.

Luke made no attempt to come any nearer. She sensed that he was fighting for control, but he couldn't feel any worse than she did!

'It wasn't planned, Kate,' he said.

'Then you'll be able to come up with an explanation —for all this,' she said drily, the sweep of her hand encompassing the office. 'I want to know why I'm here. Better still, Luke, you can tell me why *you* are here.' He moved fractionally towards her and she stepped back. 'Stay exactly where you are.'

For a second she caught the faint gleam of mockery in her eyes. 'What's the matter, Kate? Nervous?'

To deny it would have been ludicrous, even so, her colour deepened. 'I'm still waiting for an explanation,' she insisted. 'You don't get out of it so easily, Luke. I was told I had to meet a Mr Kiriakides.'

'That doesn't necessarily mean you were lied to, Kate.'

Her chin rose. 'I'm prepared to be convinced.'

'Andreas Kiriakides is my grandfather.'

For some reason she couldn't even begin to explain, Kate felt an odd sensation of relief. 'Y-your grandfather?'

He watched the varying emotions racing over her face. 'We both know I didn't have to bring you here in order to make love to you, Kate,' he said softly.

The colour in her cheeks darkened. 'I always understood that Greeks held very strict moral views where their women were concerned. Obviously you're the exception.'

Amusement crinkled the corners of his eyes. 'I haven't made love to you yet, Kate. At least, not in the very truest sense of the word. Perhaps you should reserve judgement until it happens.'

The cool confidence in his eyes made her pulses quicken. 'It won't happen,' she told him flatly, praying he believed it!

His expression was unreadable. 'My grandfather still wants to see you, Kate.'

She gave him a level look. 'I'm not at all sure that I want to see him.' A frown momentarily etched its way into her forehead. 'What could I possibly have to say to him?'

'What do you want to say?'

She threw him a scathing look. She could think of a number of things, but none of them the sort of thing she could say aloud!

'I was under the impression that I was here to discuss the report.' She licked dry lips. 'I take it you have read it?'

'Read and approved it.'

Here eyes widened. 'Just like that? Without comments?'

'I like what you came up with. You have some good ideas, soundly presented. The gallery idea in particular I thought very innovative.'

'You really liked it?' She failed to keep the gleam of pleasure out of her eyes.

'As a concept, I'm fully prepared to back it.'

She laughed shakily. 'I don't know what to say, except . . . so why am I here?'

'Because my grandfather asked to see you.'

She eyed him warily. 'You mean, I have to win his approval, too?'

The dark eyes narrowed enigmatically. 'Something like that, Kate.'

'I see—a sort of trial by jury.' Kate almost choked as she fought to control her temper. 'Damn you, Luke Redmond, you have no right to do this to me! I've a good mind to walk out of here and catch the first plane back to England. You can keep your contract. Sue me, I really don't care.'

His hand encircled her wrist as she made for the door. 'I can't let you do that, Kate.'

'I really don't see that you have any choice. I'm through playing your games.'

'Kate, my grandfather had a heart attack, just over a week ago.'

She stopped struggling. 'Oh, no! I'm so sorry. I don't know what to say.' So that was why he hadn't called! She swallowed hard. 'H-how is he?'

'He's fighting, because that's the sort of man he is. It was a pretty bad attack. When my cousin called to tell me, it was very much touch and go.'

She frowned, trying to take it all in. 'But he will be all right? I . . . I know how much he means to you.'

'They say the main danger period has passed. I gather the tenth day can be a critical time as well, which is why I want to see him again.'

She looked up at him, seeing the lines of weariness etched into his face. 'But surely he can't still want to see me?'

'He still has all his faculties, Kate.' Luke's mouth twisted. 'He may be old, but he's still head of the family and the company, and Greeks are fiercely proud.'

She straightened her shoulders and nodded. 'I'll be ready whenever you want to leave. I only need to pack a few of my things. Just let me know.'

'I'd like to leave first thing in the morning.'

She nodded again, pausing in the open doorway. He had already turned away and was standing with his hands in his pockets, staring out of the window. 'I . . . I really am sorry, Luke.'

He shrugged without turning to look at her. 'So am I, Kate,' he said softly. 'So am I.'

It was only as she hurried back to her room to begin putting things into her suitcase, that it occurred to her to wonder if they had both been talking about the same thing!

The early morning sun was already gathering heat as the open-topped car wound its way along the narrow mountain roads, and Kate was glad she had chosen to wear the thin silky shirt with her cotton skirt. Even so, she shifted uncomfortably as a tiny rivulet of sweat ran down her back.

'Why don't you make yourself more comfortable?' He took his eyes momentarily from the road to look down at her. 'Go to sleep if you want to. I know the road, and I'm not one of those drivers who need constant conversation.'

Glancing from beneath her lashes at the firm

profile, Kate tried to define whether he meant he *preferred* silence. Personally, she found it unnerving, or perhaps that was just down to the proximity of Luke beside her. A small sports car didn't allow for distance between driver and passenger.

Flushing slightly, she rested her head back and closed her eyes, not to sleep, but with the deliberate intention of trying to shut him out of her mind.

Sometime later, he manoeuvred a tight bend and, caught unawares, she slid towards him, her body making solid contact with the muscular hardness of his thigh. Straightening up quickly, she tore herself away, her throat tightening as the scent of musk aftershave on the white jacket he was wearing evoked memories she would far rather had lain dormant. Flushing hotly, she sat back, bracing herself in the seat.

'Sorry.'

His mouth tightened briefly. 'Go back to sleep. You must be exhausted.'

She sat up rigidly. 'It must be the heat. I didn't mean to drop off like that. I thought I'd only closed my eyes for a few seconds.'

'You slept for an hour, Kate.'

'Oh.' Her eyes met his, and there was a slight movement at the corners of his mouth.

'Don't worry about it. I can drive quite safely with your head resting against my shoulder. You aren't exactly heavy, Kate.'

She turned away quickly, staring in confusion at a scene which, she knew already, would stay imprinted in her mind for ever. Even the light seemed different as the sun rose in the sky, its heat hanging over the mountains and valleys in a silent blue haze.

Inhaling deeply, she tried to pinpoint an elusive perfume and, as if he sensed her thoughts, Luke nodded towards the distance. 'If you're trying to locate the scent, it comes from the trees. Those are almond orchards down there in the valley. You'll probably see some vineyards and lemon trees, too.'

Her heartbeat seemed to quicken from sheer joy and wonderment. 'What about those other trees? They seem to be everywhere, thousands of them.'

'Millions,' he corrected gently. 'Those are olives. Some as old as the Bible itself.'

She turned to him, smiling disbelief. 'Surely that isn't possible?'

Luke kept his gaze on the steeply twisting road. 'Some of the oldest would have been planted as saplings in the time of Christ.' Now he looked at her. 'It does rather force you to look at things in a whole new perspective, doesn't it?'

Kate sat silently digesting the thought that that was precisely what she seemed to have been doing from the minute she had met him—and it hadn't got her very far.

His voice cut across her thoughts, and she had to blink hard before she could force herself to look at him. 'Sorry, did you say something?' For a brief moment, she wondered what caused the slight tightening of his mouth before he shook his head.

'It wasn't important.' He glanced at his watch. 'We're almost there. You'll be able to relax soon.'

Was her state of tension so apparent? she wondered.

Almost as he said it, it seemed, the car turned in through the gates of a high, white villa, and slid to a halt on the drive. Kate had barely time to catch a glimpse of flower-strewn walls before he was climbing out of the car and holding her door open. For a moment she hung back, suddenly reluctant to intrude. So this was his home. Kate was conscious of a nagging ache deep within herself. A feeling she decided it was far safer not to pursue.

'Are you going to get out, Kate?' his voice came down to her. 'Or do you plan on sitting there for the duration?'

Scarlet-cheeked, she scrambled out only to find that, instead of moving, he had reached out a lazy, confident arm, trapping her against the car.

'I just want you to know that I'm not giving up on you, Kate.'

Something about the way he said it sent a sudden tremor running down her spine. Reassurance? Or threat? Her startled gaze flew up to meet his, but the question was never asked, as a tall, slender figure came running down the steps towards them and, without as much as a glance in Kate's direction, flung herself into Luke's eagerly waiting arms.

Kate had to look away as jealousy seared through her with the heat and intensity of a forest fire, its violence threatening to choke her.

CHAPTER ELEVEN

KATE stood motionless, waiting for the moment when the two would break apart and remember her presence, and in the interlude found herself staring in rapt fascination at the girl from whom Luke was now gently but unhurriedly detaching himself.

Swallowing a painful lump in her throat, Kate had to admit that she was lovely. Evenly tanned, with dark hair swept back from her face, the girl was typically Greek. It might have been easier if she could have found something to dislike, Kate told herself with an alien resentment, but there was nothing as the brown eyes looked perceptively in her direction.

'And this . . . must be Kate.' The girl smiled and said something softly in Greek. It had sounded friendly enough but, whatever it was, Kate was surprised by the sudden ominous tightening of Luke's features as he reached into the car for her suitcase.

'We're both hot, Maria, and Kate is tired. How is my grandfather?'

'Sleeping peacefully. He seems a little better.' Maria muttered something again in Greek, crossing herself as she did so. 'Nikos is sitting with him.' She led Kate through an archway into the cool, tiled interior of the house, frowning slightly. 'Nikos makes his apology. He is anxious to greet you, but later, perhaps, we all

163

eat together.'

Kate threw a confused glance at Luke. 'Nikos?'

'Nikos is married to my cousin Maria,' Luke drawled softly. 'Did I forget to tell you?' Mocking laughter lurked in his eyes.

Kate managed a tight-lipped smile. 'You may have done, I really can't remember.' The sudden contact of his hand against her arm sent a tiny quiver of excitement running through her, but she managed to detach herself from his grasp and smile at Maria. 'As a matter of fact, I'm not tired at all, just rather hot and thirsty.'

'I have refreshments ready prepared. Some fresh lemonade, or perhaps you would prefer tea?'

'No, really, lemonade sounds marvellous.'

Maria smiled. 'Come then, please be comfortable. Out here you will be cool.' She led them out to a terrace, and Kate couldn't contain a quiet gasp of pleasure as she saw a large swimming pool.

'You like to swim?' Luke said.

Kate shrugged. 'I enjoy it—on holiday. Our climate doesn't exactly allow for this kind of luxury, as you must have noticed.'

Maria came out to the terrace again, carrying a tray of glasses and a jug which she deposited on the table. 'Please,' she looked shyly at Kate, 'while you are here, you must think of this villa as your own. I know Luke will wish it.'

Kate blushed. 'Thank you, that's very kind but . . .'

'I swim every morning when I'm here.' It was Luke who poured the drinks and handed her a glass.

'This is true,' Maria confirmed wryly. 'Sometimes

I think he never sleeps.'

Kate stolidly refused to meet his gaze. 'I never have any trouble myself, but then, that's possible because I have a clear conscience.'

She heard the rasp of what may have been laughter in his throat. 'I find waking early has its advantages. You should try it.'

She swirled her drink furiously in her glass. 'I'd hate to spoil your routine.'

'But it's not my routine that's in danger, Kate.' The softly spoken words were barely audible, but her heart suddenly started beating in a highly erratic fashion. Rising briskly to her feet, she set her glass on the tray.

'If you don't mind, I'd really rather like to go to my room and freshen up.' Having addressed herself deliberately to Maria, she had to bite back a sigh of frustration as Luke immediately rose to his feet.

'Good idea,' he drawled, raised eyebrows deliberately mocking her. 'I could use a cold shower myself right now.'

Afraid—or unwilling—to interpret the glint in the dark eyes, Kate turned her back purposefully on him to hurry after Maria, telling herself that she hadn't heard the whispered 'coward' or his following laughter.

Maria opened a door and Kate followed her into the bedroom. 'I hope you will be comfortable. You must say if there is anything you wish.'

'Oh, no, it's beautiful.' A carefully arranged display of flowers had been placed on a table beside the bed, but it was the bed itself which drew her attention, and warm colour suffused her cheeks as Luke came slowly towards her. Her breathing quickened. 'I thought you wanted to take a cold shower?'

The sardonic gaze swept her face. 'Not wanted, Kate, *needed*. There's a subtle difference. Would you like me to prove it to you?'

Maria stood in the open doorway, her gaze flitting uncertainly from one to the other. 'I leave you to unpack and be comfortable. I must go to Grand-papa

'Please, don't worry, I'm sure I can manage.' Kate looked determinedly at Luke, and drew a panic-filled breath as he made no attempt to leave. He was the most powerfully sexual man she had ever known, and she had never been more physically aware of him than at this precise moment.

She closed her eyes tightly, knowing that if he were to kiss her she wouldn't be able to resist. She felt his hand brush against her tightly closed eyelids, then smoothing a tendril of hair from her cheek. But the kiss didn't come.

Her eyes flew open to meet his, then away again as she realised he was frowning. She stood frozen, unable to move. She *wanted* him to kiss her. She broke away, her eyes blurred, and took a deep breath as she saw the look of taut strain on his features—as if he knew precisely what she had been thinking.

He stunned gaze followed him to the door, and it was only the sudden realisation that he was leaving that gave her back her voice.

'Luke, I . . . Where are you going?'

He looked suddenly impatient. 'I really do need that shower.'

'Yes, but . . .'

A muscle tightened in his jaw. 'My room is only next door, Kate. If you need me, you have only to call.' He turned smartly on his heel and walked away, leaving Kate feeling as if she had been struck by lightning. For several minutes after he had gone, she sat on the bed, shaking. Then the thought hit her like a huge tidal wave. She was in love with him!

Shocked by the admission, she pressed a trembling hand to her mouth. In spite of all the self-made promises, somehow it had happened. All this time she had been afraid to fall in love, and the irony now was that the only man ever to break through her defences had made it perfectly clear that it wasn't *love* he wanted!

Kate spent a long time over her unpacking, and waited until there was no sound from the adjoining room and she was sure Luke must have gone downstairs before she finally risked going into the shower. Even then, it wasn't possible to wash away the aching torment his nearness had created. His presence was everywhere still, lingering in the faint fragrance of the cologne he had used after taking his shower. It was something which would stay in her mind long after she had returned to England and her own face was just a blur in his memory.

But at least the shower had gone some way towards reviving her physically, and by the time she had slipped into clean white undies, white cotton trousers and a shirt which she knotted at the waist, she was feeling slightly more human as she went downstairs and out to the terrace.

Having steeled herself to see Luke, it came as a relief to find Maria sitting alone by the poolside. The girl had obviously been for a swim. Her hair was sleeked damply back, and she had pulled a short robe on over her bikini.

She smiled shyly as Kate joined her. 'I thought you might want to sleep. In Greece, everyone goes home until the sun is less hot. Even the shops and offices close until four o'clock.'

'That explains why Athens seemed so quiet when I arrived.' Grinning, Kate lowered herself into one of the white chairs.

'I'm afraid Nikos has had to leave. He was sorry not to see you, but tonight at dinner you will definitely meet.'

'I look forward to it.' The more the merrier, Kate thought bleakly. 'What does your husband do?'

'He is a doctor in the city, but while *papo,*' she gave a quick smile of apology, 'why Grandpapa is so ill he has been coming home to sit with him.' She rose to her feet. 'You haven't eaten. There is some salad and fruit.'

'No, really, I'm still not very hungry. I just seem to feel permanently thirsty.'

'It's a good thing to drink in this heat. There's iced coffee in the jug, but I can always get something else.'

'No, please,' Kate protested. 'The coffee looks

delicious.' She sipped at the contents of the long glass Maria handed her, and nodded her approval. 'Mmm, it's superb.'

'Perhaps you would like to sit in the shade. I forget you're not yet used to our climate . . .'

'I suppose it might be wiser.' Not that she was going to have time to get used to it, Kate thought, as she followed Maria along the terrace. Its edges were a confusion of trailing colours which continued through gardens and even in huge terracotta tubs, as Maria led her up an external staircase and into a drawing-room.

Kate gasped her pleasure as her designer's eye took in the brilliance of reds against stark white and grey. 'You have a beautiful home.'

'Not mine, but Luke's,' Maria smiled, 'although he seldom lives here now.'

Kate looked at her in some confusion. 'Oh, I see, I'm sorry, obviously I misunderstood.'

'You didn't know?' Maria sent her a slanting glance. 'Luke bought the villa several years ago.'

'Yes, of course, I suppose now that he has to be in England he dosn't have time to come here as often as he must wish. He must miss it dreadfully.' How could anyone not? she thought wistfully.

'I suppose in time he may wish to come back,' Maria said. 'For now, he is happy that his grandpapa can be here.' She smiled sadly. 'The old man is very strong-willed, in spite of his years. He was determined they would not take him to the hosiptal. And who knows, perhaps he was right, he would have died all the sooner in a strange place with strangers around him.' Her hand rose. 'In any event, Luke would never permit it to happen.'

'I can understand why he is so worried.'

Maria nodded. 'They have always been close. Luke is sitting with him now. Sometimes I think he feels he must make the most of the time they may have left.'

Kate toyed with her glass, conscious of a slight feeling of guilt that they should be discussing Luke in his absence. 'His grandfather must have been an exceptional man, to have raised a small child more or less single-handed.'

'Luke has talked to you about himself?' Maria eyed her perceptively.

'No, not really, only that his parents died when he was still very young.'

'Then he has told you more than most.'

Kate flushed. 'He doesn't strike me as the sort of man who exchanges confidences easily.'

'Luke is a very private person. Few people know what his feelings are, because he chooses to hide them. In many ways, he and his grandpapa are very much alike.'

'You mean they are both strong-willed?' Kate couldn't resist.

Maria laughed softly and, rising from her chair, crossed to the bookshelf. 'That, and in looks also.' Returning to where Kate sat, she handed her an open snapshot album. 'You can see the resemblance here, very early on. Luke was no more than ten when this picture was taken, but already the likeness is there.'

Gazing at the picture of a young boy standing on a beach beside an older man, Kate felt her throat tighten. 'Yes, I see what you mean.'

'They were always together. They shared everything, even the tragedies in their lives.'

Kate turned the pages, conscious of a feeling almost of intrusion, and yet she felt drawn to go on, to experience this part of his life she had never dared hope to see. 'He must have missed his parents dreadfully.

'His father perhaps less so than his mother,' Maria admitted sadly. 'He was very young when his father died, but her death hit him very hard. I remember he tried not to weep when they told him.'

Kate's hand shook as she turned the page. They were the sort of pictures one would find in any family album, yet, for some reason, her eyes filled with tears.

She had to blink hard as she came to another study of Luke, again with his grandfather, but now they were older and this time there was a girl, a lovely girl with long, black hair, shading her eyes from the sun as she smiled directly into the camera. Luke's arm was draped lazily around her bare shoulders, and something in his expression as he gazed down at her sent a pang of sheer jealousy searing through Kate.

Almost as if anticipating the question, an odd expression crossed Maria's face. After a brief pause, she said quietly, 'Ah, yes, that is Eleni.'

Kate swallowed the painful tightness in her throat. 'She's lovely.'

'Yes.' Maria suddenly closed the book, returning it to the shelf. 'It was no surprise to anyone when Luke asked her to be his wife.'

Kate felt the colour leaving her face. 'His . . . Luke has a wife?'

Maria gave her a sharp look. 'She was just eighteen when they were married. I remember the whole village joined in the celebrations.' She broke off. 'Are you all right?'

Kate nodded. Maria's voice seemed to be coming from somewhere far away. She rose shakily to her feet. 'Yes, I'm fine. You were telling me . . . about the wedding.'

'There is little more to say.' Maria's hand rose. 'A year later, she was dead.' Maria stopped suddenly, a look of dismay filling her eyes. 'But I thought you knew this.'

Kate swallowed convulsively. 'No, I . . .' She closed her eyes, trying to shut out a horrifying vision of the pain he must have suffered, and a wave of compassion filled her. If only she had known—could have guessed!

'H-how did it happen?' She saw the moment's hesitation in the other girl's eyes. 'I would . . . I need to know.'

'It was a car. The road has so many twists and turns.' Maria's eyes glittered. 'She was on her way to meet Luke. The other car came towards her. Before he saw her, it was already too late. She was dead before anyone could reach her.' Maria looked at Kate. 'I I had realised you knew nothing of this . . . . I was so sure Luke must have told you.'

'There was no reason for him to have done so.' Kate blinked hard. 'I only work for him, you know.'

Maria looked perceptively at her, and for a moment her brow furrowed. 'I think perhaps Luke has learned to conceal his feelings too well.'

'But he has no reason to hide them from me.'

'Perhaps even more so from you.' Maria spoke the words with a sudden measure of shyness. 'It might be easier if he felt nothing for you, because then he would have no fear of being hurt.' She watched the colour darkening Kate's cheeks. 'You love him, do you not?'

Kate licked her dry lips before saying bleakly, 'Very much.'

'Then all will be well. Whatever troubles there are between you can be swept away.'

'I'm not sure it can be that simple.'

'Then perhaps you must make it so. Sometimes pain can become a habit, a cloak almost, to conceal what is real and may be dangerous. Luke is not a coward. Perhaps he also needs to be sure of your feelings for him, before he can make himself vulnerable again.'

Kate nodded slowly, her eyes stinging with unshed tears as, in an impulsive gesture, she went to hug the girl.

'I hope you're right.'

'About what?'

It was Luke's voice coming quietly from behind her which brought the colour rushing into her cheeks, and she turned swiftly to face him.

'Secrets, Kate?' He raised dark eyebrows, and Kate was grateful for the normality in Maria's voice as she answered for her.

'It is woman's talk, *mana mou,* nothing to interest you.'

His face seemed drawn and suddenly gaunt as he looked at Kate. 'My grandfather has asked to see you, if you want to go to him now. Don't stay too long,' he warned. 'He likes to talk, but he still tires very easily.'

'Don't worry,' she said evenly. 'I won't encourage him.'

'It's a pity you can't offer some guarantee of immunity to the rest of us,' he ground out savagely. But, before she could even begin to give voice to a stunned protest, he was striding away, leaving her to gaze in anguish after his fast retreating figure.

Entering the room in answer to a quiet summons, Kate found herself hesitating as her shocked gaze registered not the product of her imaginings, but a head of snow-white hair and a face in which, despite all the evidence of his illness, the eyes still remained acutely alert and mobile.

'*Kyria* Langley. Please come closer,' his voice beckoned, and Kate went towards the chair where he sat by an open window, feeling a spasm of compassion tighten her throat as he held out his hand. She placed her own in it and smiled. Andreas Kiriakides in his eightieth year was still a striking figure of a man.

'You must forgive me for not greeting you upon your arrival.' He indicated a chair. 'Please, sit beside me. I would get up, but it would only set Maria to fussing and my grandson to summoning my old mule of a doctor.' The gentle humour behind his eyes sent a dull ache through Kate as she began to understand something of the closeness between this man and Luke. Maria had been right, she thought. Despite the distance of years, they were alike.

She smiled. 'They love you very much. I'm sure

they do only what they feel is best.'

He waved a hand deprecatingly. 'Cosseting is for tender young plants, not old men.' He leaned forwards, the action causing a spasm of coughing, and Kate half rose to her feet in concern.

'You're tired. Perhaps you should get some sleep. I can always come back later.'

Andreas Kiriakides chuckled, waving her back to her seat. 'What I would like is some brandy, but my grandson prefers to listen to my doctor, who is even older than I and who never enjoyed the taste of good liquor in his life.'

In spite of herself, Kate smiled. 'I think it's what any doctor would advise, at least until you feel a little stronger. Can I get you something else? A glass of orange juice, or some iced water perhaps?'

He dismissed the suggestion with a snort of impatience. 'Even my taste for brandy is not what it was.' He sat back, studying her face. 'I'm tired. Tell me about yourself. Talk to me, *mana mou*.'

'I'm afraid there's very little to tell,' Kate protested. 'You would find it very boring.'

He laughed, and there was a frailty in the sound which alarmed her. 'At my age, when every minute is precious, even to be bored is a blessing. But I think you are unjust to yourself, child.'

Faint colour darkened her cheeks. 'What would you like to hear?'

'Whatever you choose to tell me,' he said softly. 'I have no wish to intrude.'

But that was precisely what he was doing! Kate fought a momentary flicker of irritation, which was instantly replaced by one of guilt, and she felt herself blush. 'I wasn't thinking of it as an intrusion, it's just that, compared to what you have here, where everything is so beautiful, a small, rather ancient house in an English suburb must seem rather boring.'

'Do you find it boring?'

Kate met the shrewd gaze and smiled. 'No, as a matter of fact, I love it. At the end of a hard day, especially when I've had to battle through the infernal British traffic, there's something very reassuring about being able to close my own front door on the world.'

'In Greece, that can also be true.' He chuckled softly before the dark gaze settled again on her face. 'You live alone?'

Kate met his gaze directly. 'Yes. It may seem old-fashioned by today's standards . . .'

'In my country, a man still believes it his duty to guard his woman's honour.'

'His woman?' Kate drew a deep breath. 'You make her sound like a piece of property, something to be fought over, whether she likes it or not.'

'The thought offends you?'

She frowned. 'I don't think I could accept the idea of being owned, that's all.'

'No Greek woman would feel this way.'

'But I'm not Greek.'

Andreas Kiriakides smiled. 'All women secretly wish to know that their man will protect them. Even when it is only from their own foolishness.' He leaned forwards and smiled. 'My grandson is right, you *are* beautiful. All the more reason you should have the protection of a strong man.'

Kate's eyes widened. 'I don't think . . . that is . . .'

He frowned. 'It shocks you that my grandson finds you beautiful?'

'No.' She bit at her lip. 'Not exactly.'

'Then you are offended that he talks to me of his feelings.'

Her chin rose. 'I think you may have misunderstood his feelings.'

A frail hand came to rest over her own. 'Tell me, *mana mou,*' he said quietly, 'why are you here?'

Kate blinked. 'Because . . . because I was told you wish to see me.'

Brown eyes twinkled. 'This is true. An old man is allowed his curiosity. So—now I have seen you.'

'But . . . I thought . . . that is, I understood I was here to discuss the designs for Poseidon UK.'

'Ah!' He nodded. 'My grandson told you this?'

Kate swallowed a painful tightness in her throat. 'I understood that your approval was necessary.'

An odd expression crossed the old man's face. 'My grandson is in many ways more Greek than even he would choose to admit.'

Kate frowned. 'I don't understand. What has his being Greek to do with any of this?'

'Perhaps more than even I had realised,' he said softly. 'There is only one reason why Luke would wish for my approval. Only once before he asked it, when he brought to me the girl he wished to marry.' His hand tightened over Kate's. 'I began to think he would never find happiness again. He has no need of my blessing, but I give it gladly.'

Kate's mouth felt dry as she stared at him. 'Y-you don't understand. Luke doesn't want to marry me. He doesn't love me.'

Andreas Kiriakides touched her cheek, and suddenly she realised that he was gently wiping away tears. 'Does he tell you this?'

She shook her head, the hot colour coming into her cheeks. 'He doesn't need to say it.'

He gave her a quick look which was almost arrogant in its disapproval. 'You know my grandson so well that you can read his mind—better than I who raised him?'

Tears welled in her green eyes now. 'I know how deeply he loved Eleni.' She heard the sharp intake of his breath. 'What he feels for me could never compare. I know I couldn't take her place, and I wouldn't presume to try.'

'Tell me, *mana mou,* do you love my grandson?'

She drew a deep, shuddering breath. 'Yes.'

'Then why have you so little faith in him?' He shook his head. 'I know there has been tragedy in your own life.'

'Y-you know?'

'To Luke, I am the father he lost. He tells me those things which are closest to his heart, and he speaks of you. If you, in spite of everything, have found room in your heart for my grandson, then why is it so difficult to believe that he can do the same?'

Kate shook her head and rose slowly to her feet. 'Because it isn't the same.' She drew a ragged breath. 'I had stopped loving my husband even before he died. I didn't want it to happen. I tried not to let it happen.'

'Sometimes we are given no choice.'

'But don't you see?' Kate sighed. 'Luke still loves Eleni, and I don't think I can bear it.' Without a backward glance she ran from the room, still blinded by tears, so that she was barely aware of the grim-faced figure who stood there or who called her name.

Once within the safety of her room, Kate flung herself on to the bed and wept in earnest: deep, painful sobs which racked her body with such intensity that she wasn't even aware of the door opening until a hand brushed the hair from her cheek. She raised startled eyes to gaze into Luke's gaunt face.

For a moment she lay staring at him through a blur of tears, telling herself that he couldn't possibly be there, any more than she could be seeing the expression in his dark, pain-filled eyes. Then he was beside her, gathering her in his arms, his weight above her as he kissed her with an urgency which was both brutal and relentless.

'Kate. Oh, Kate!' he moaned savagely as his lips burned over her mouth, against her hair, his hands cupping her face as he forced her to look at him. 'For God's sake, don't cry. I can't bear it,' he groaned as her tears fell still faster. She wasn't even certain why she was crying, except that she loved him, and now that he was actually with her it no longer seemed to matter that he didn't want her love. In one blinding flash of realisation, she knew she would settle for what he was prepared to give, even though some day it must end. For now, it was enough that he was here and that she loved him. Later—much later, she would think of losing him.

Without thinking, she arched herself against him, returning his kiss, demanding more, and for one moment she felt his body tense above hers. With a desperate urgency she began tugging at the buttons of his shirt, until her fingers could begin their urgent tracing of his shoulders, feeling his body quiver in reaction.

'Luke, make love to me,' she murmured, her hands feverishly pushing aside the barrier of clothing which was between them. She sensed rather than saw the shock widening his eyes as he stared down at her, restraining her hands.

'Kate, for God's sake, do you know what you're doing?'

Her arms reached up, drawing him towards her, and with a groan his mouth possessed hers in a fierce, sensuous arousal. 'I know, I know,' she murmured against his shoulder.

'Kate, I hope you're not going to regret this,' he moaned as his lips explored the curve of her throat, moving to her breasts as his hands tore aside the flimsy restrictions of her shirt. 'God knows, I want you,' he said huskily, 'but you'd better be warned . . . I don't think I'm going to be able to stop if you change your mind.'

As if in answer, her mouth moved from his face to begin teasing at his throat and chest, and she almost revelled in his harsh groans of protest as her hands continued to make a gentle, still nervous exploration of his body. 'I won't change my mind.' Her hands cupped his face, forcing him to look at her. She lay beneath him, their bodies now free of the last barrier as their clothes lay discarded on the floor.

She could feel the heat of his skin against her own, the taut arousal of his body, which said more clearly than words how much he wanted her.

'You once said I'd have to come to you,' she said softly.

'Is that why . . .' He lifted his head, and she silenced his words with her fingers.

'Make love to me. The reasons don't matter.' Her hands stroked his shoulders, the nails digging into the muscular flesh, and she felt him shudder uncontrollably as she deliberately continued the movement along his spine.

'Oh, God . . .' His voice was muffled against her throat, and she knew from the throbbing urgency of his arousal that *she* held the power, that, in spite of his physical male strength, at this moment he was the more vulnerable.

His voice was hoarse as he drew her towards him, caressing her body, moulding her to him until it seemed they became one, and in the moment of possession her swift cry of pleasure brought his mouth back to hers, heavy with loving, their moist, heated bodies stilled now, but still entwined as the convulsive waves of their lovemaking became calm.

For a long time she lay in his arms, exhausted yet exhilarated. It was only when she turned to look at Luke, thinking he must have fallen asleep, that she realised, blushing, that he was studying her, the dark eyes glittering as they roamed every centimetre of her naked, glowing body, and she felt herself shiver with excitement as he turned towards her again.

She responded with an immediacy and an eagerness she had never believed possible, even though she still felt drugged and pleasure-filled from that first sweet, sensuous invasion. But this time, when he drew her close, she sensed that he was deliberately controlling the powerful tensions still throbbing within him.

She reached out a hand, running her fingers exultantly over his chest, lower and lower still until, with a groan, he seized her fingers, stilling their exquisite torment.

In one swift movement he had pinned her beneath him, and this time there was no doubt about his superiority. 'Now it's my turn, Kate,' he breathed. 'But first you're going to have to explain. I've wanted you too long, had you fight me . . .'

'Are you saying that you have regrets for what just happened?' A tiny flicker of fear widened her eyes, and she heard him swear softly.

'I'll prove that I have no regrets, very soon. Right now, I just need to know that you aren't going to disappear, like some beautiful dream, the minute I let you go.' His eyes darkened. 'My God, if I thought that might happen I'd never let you go, Kate,' he rasped.

Her body quivered so violently with her need of him that her breathing was ragged. 'I won't disappear,' she told him huskily. 'I realised suddenly that you were right when you said I couldn't run away for ever, that I had to face reality.' She swallowed hard as tears threatened to well up in her eyes.

For a long, tense moment he looked down at her,

before sliding down beside her. 'I said a lot of things,' he muttered the protest against her hair as he kissed her with surprising restraint. 'Things I had no right to say.'

She put her arms out, drawing his head towards her breast. 'But you were right. I just didn't want to admit it.' She drew a ragged breath as she forced herself to look at him. 'I was scared of having it happen all over again, don't you see? I told myself I wasn't going to be hurt a second time.'

'And you thought *I* would hurt you? Is that what you're saying?' His mouth hardened, and she felt the tears stinging at the back of her throat.

'I couldn't take the risk.'

'What did he do to you, Kate?' he demanded softly. 'What sort of hold could he have that made you even think you could sacrifice the rest of your life to the memory of a dead man?'

She tried to cover her face as humiliation washed over her like a huge, suffocating wave, but he wouldn't let her.

'Tell me, Kate. Lay his ghost once and for all.'

She drew a long, quivering breath. 'Steve's death was my fault.'

He seemed to freeze over her. 'That's crazy,' he said tersely. 'How could you possibly be to blame?'

She had to force herself to look at him. 'Perhaps not directly, but maybe I could have done something— *should* have done something to prevent it.'

His dark eyes glittered as he stared down at her. 'How in hell could you have done that?'

'I don't know,' she protested, feeling her eyes fill

with tears. 'Perhaps . . . if I'd loved him more . . . h-he might not have started to drink.'

Luke's mouth tightened grimly. 'He was drunk? My God, what . . . did he hurt you?'

She had to look away from him now. 'It all happened so gradually. At first, he just started to lose his temper.' Her mouth quivered. 'Ironically, I think he began to resent me, even the fact that I gave up my own career so that he could carry on with his painting.' She shuddered. 'One day he actually hit me. The day he died, he had been drinking. Oh, he denied it, he always did, but by then I knew all the signs, and anyway I could smell it on him.' She gave a brittle laugh. 'In some ways, he was so naïve. He really imagined I coudn't tell. Or . . . or perhaps he stopped caring.'

She frowned and was silent for a moment. 'I hid the car keys to stop him taking the car. It didn't fool him. He guessed what I'd done and started demanding them, and when I refused to hand them over, he knocked me to the floor. I don't think he meant it,' she said quickly. 'I just don't think he knew his own strength. Anyway, I must have been stunned for a few seconds, but it was enough. By the time I could try to stop him, it was too late. He had obviously found my handbag, tipped the contents out, and taken the keys.' She swallowed hard. 'He didn't get more than a hundred yards. The police came to tell me. They were very kind and understanding, they said he had died instantly. The car hit a tree.'

She was sobbing quietly, and with a curse Luke took her in his arms. He lay with her body pressed against him, hugging her close, rocking her gently. 'I'm sorry, Kate. I should have understood.' He lowered his face to kiss her, smoothing the hair from her cheek, and she saw his eyes widen as if in some dawning realisation. 'Is that why you don't drink alcohol?'

'I can't.' Her throat tightened. 'It makes me sick.'

He groaned softly. 'But how can you blame yourself for what happened? You couldn't stop him drinking. Even his resentment of you wasn't logical.'

'But, don't you see, perhaps if I'd loved him more . . .

'It wasn't your fault that he destroyed whatever there might have been between you, Kate. You have to face the fact that some people are weak. It doesn't matter what hand they're dealt, they always turn out to be losers. I'm not a loser. What we have is good and real.'

And it would have to be enough. It *would* be enough, she told herself, for as long as it lasted. And when it was over she would have her memories. It seemed her life was full of them.

'Kate, what is it?' Forcing her to look at him, Luke was shocked by the bleak misery in her eyes.

'I . . . I know about . . . about Eleni.'

She waited for the anger to darken his face. Instead, he bent his head to kiss her mouth.

'I know. Maria confessed in a state of panic that she had told you, imagining that you already knew.'

'But don't you mind?' She stared at him and saw his eyes narrow.

'Why should I mind you knowing, Kate? True, I

loved Eleni. She was lovely and gentle, and the brief time we spent together was . . .' he drew a ragged breath '. . . was so perfect, I didn't think I'd ever be able to face the rest of my life without her.'

Kate's fingers closed convulsively against his skin. She wanted to cry as a tight ball of pain filled her chest. 'I know . . . I know I could never take her place, but it doesn't matter. You were right. What we have is good, and it's real,' her voice rasped thickly, 'and it's time I faced reality again. I want to face it with you. I don't even care how long it lasts, a day, a week . . .'

Suddenly he had tensed above her, and Kate shivered beneath the brilliant fury in his eyes. 'What the hell are you trying to say?' His hands tightened on her shoulders so that she flinched with pain.

She swallowed convulsively. 'I just want you to know that . . . I don't mind. That I'll be whatever you want, for as long as you want.'

'For God's sake!' He was shaking her, then, with a husky oath, his mouth closed over hers in a kiss that seemed to burn itself not only on to her lips but into her soul as well. She went with him, giving herself totally to the fierceness of his desire and matching it with her own, giving a soft whimper of protest as he broke away for a few seconds to look down at her. 'I want you for as long as there is, for all of eternity and beyond. Everything there is of you and more. I love you, Kate.' He ran his hands over her body, stroking, seducing. 'I intend to prove it to you now, but I warn you, there's no escape.' He lifted her up to meet him, and her arms went round his neck.

'I'm where I want to be,' she told him softly.

'No more barriers, Kate?'

'No more barriers,' she promised, offering her own proof in the only way she knew how.

Harlequin American Romance

Romances that go one step farther...
American Romance

Realistic stories involving people you can relate to and care about.

Compelling relationships between the mature men and women of today's world.

Romances that capture the core of genuine emotions between a man and a woman.

Join us each month for four new titles wherever paperback books are sold.
Enter the world of American Romance.

Amro-1

Harlequin Temptation dares to be different!

Once in a while, we Temptation editors spot a romance that's truly innovative. To make sure *you* don't miss any one of these outstanding selections, we'll mark them for you.

EDITOR'S CHOICE

When the "Editors' Choice" fold-back appears on a Temptation cover, you'll know we've found that extra-special page-turner!

THE *Temptation*

EDITORS

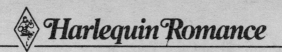 **Harlequin Romance**

Coming Next Month

**Available in February wherever paperback books are sold, or
through Harlequin Reader Service:**

In the U.S.
901 Fuhrmann Blvd.
P.O. Box 1397
Buffalo, N.Y. 14240-1397

In Canada
P.O. Box 603
Fort Erie, Ontario
L2A 5X3

 Harlequin Books

You're never too young to
enjoy romance. Harlequin
for you . . . and Keepsake,
young-adult romances
destined to win hearts, for
your daughter.

Pick one up today and
start your daughter on her
journey into the wonderful
world of romance.

Two new titles to choose
from each month.

ATTRACTIVE, SPACE SAVING BOOK RACK

Display your most prized novels on this handsome and sturdy book rack. The hand-rubbed walnut finish will blend into your library decor with quiet elegance, providing a practical organizer for your favorite hard-or soft-covered books.

Only
$9.95

Approximately
16" x 8"
when assembled

Assembles in seconds!

To order, rush your name, address and zip code, along with a check or money order for $10.70* ($9.95 plus 75¢ postage and handling) payable to *Harlequin Reader Service*:

Harlequin Reader Service
Book Rack Offer
901 Fuhrmann Blvd.
P.O. Box 1396
Buffalo, NY 14269-1396

Offer not available in Canada.

BKR-1A

*New York and Iowa residents add appropriate sales tax.